THE
CONFUSED
MIND OF A
DRUG DEALER

Published by Altruism Inc., Los Angeles, California
www.ConfusedMindOfADrugDealer.com

Library of Congress Catalogue

ISBN – 978-0-9841822-0-6

This book is dedicated to
my mother Mary S. Handy, my father William L. Handy
Sr., my family, and most of all to my Lord and Savior, for
granting me the journey and keeping me under His grace,
to be able to tell the story of
The Confused Mind of a Drug Dealer

I'd like to thank my editor Lea Reis for bringing my book
to life. Thanks to Gregory Watson Jr. for so many late
nights in the studio making tracks to keep me going, and
for the book cover idea. To Willie Armstrong for
bringing the book cover to life with his creative mind.
Thank you, Mashael Mariee, Nichole Wyatt, and Mia
Jackson for your time and effort.

The Confused Mind of a Drug Dealer

CONTENTS

THE CONFUSED MIND OF A DRUG DEALER

Chapter 1

Moms Get Beat

"You sure you wanna hit this lick nigga? Well fuck it, let's roll."

Man, who would've ever thought a 5'6" little mothafucka, best dressed out the D High would've been one of Compton's biggest drug dealers in the 90's? Growin' up in a family of 7 with 2 sisters, 2 brothers, moms and pops in a 3-bedroom-house-turned-into-a-2-bedroom-house-with-a-den was a mothafuckin' trip. Shit, privacy was out the question. Shit, we were always in each other's business. You know how that shit is. Well…if you don't, let me give you a run down.

Chapter 1

Like I said, there were 7 in my house. My best friend lived across the street in a household of 4; him, his moms, step-pops, and his sister. Remember I said BEST FRIEND. I was born in 1970 and anybody who knows about the 70's, knew niggas was hustlin' hoes, shootin' dice, movin' that white horse, sellin' pills. All kinds of licks were being hit back then. Shit was good then. Snitch bitches were nowhere to be found. Like Jay-Z said, "I'm from an era where niggas don't snitch."

My home was a trip. Moms and pops would go out, and return so fucked up that pops would beat the shit out of moms. Being little, and shit, I couldn't do anything. My older brother and sister would stop him, but by the time they did, moms was already fucked up and I'd think, "Damn this shit would not have happened if I was bigger." I would tell myself, "I would never hit my woman or any other woman."

Man, my pops was so fucked up one night, he beat moms worse than I had ever seen anybody get beat. He knocked the shit out of her. When she fell to the floor he started stomping her. After stomping her, he pulled her by her hair and started beating her with a shoe. My younger brother and I were so scared that we hid under the bed. Picture seeing this shit at 5 and 8 years old. All we thought was, "Moms is about to get beat to death." After he finished stomping moms and beating her with his shoe, he looked like the devil was in him. He said, "Bitch, I'm about to bash your head in." He went

2

outside and came back in with a crow bar. Just as his arms went up to swing a killing blow, my sister, 14 at the time, jumped in front of him saying, "Daddy, NO!" At that moment, God stepped in. I know it was God because pops just dropped the crowbar and walked out of the house as if nothing happened. It was finally quiet. We all ran to moms to hold and comfort her. That was all we could do. You know the crazy part? The next day he asked her, "What happened to you?!" All she said was, "You did this." He was so drunk he would never remember what the fuck he had done. As a kid, all I could think about was, "You beat her ass like this and you can't remember? What the fuck is wrong with you?" I watched my mother being beat. Her strength would make me love her more than words would say.

"Years later, sitting in the back of a police car with handcuffs on, I wondered how I ended up here."

Growing up, I attended schools in Compton, from elementary to high school. My older brother and sister paved the way, making things a little easier for me to get through. At Emerson Elementary School I was a good student. I achieved certificates in math and reading throughout the years. I didn't get into any trouble. But, I do remember being chased home every day by two boys, for an entire week. I still don't know why. One day, while being chased, I stopped

Chapter 1

and turned to one of them socking him right in the face, turning back around to run off. They never followed me again. I thanked God my parents had put me in martial arts. That lesson taught me to never run again. I learned that when you stand up for yourself you don't have to run from anyone. My father would always say, "It's not the size of the dog that wins the fight; it's the fight in the dog."

My Father. My father was a hard working, hustlin' man. He hauled scrap metal for a living. Yes, a junk man as the world would say. When I say hustlin' man, I remember days my father would use our house as a dice house. He would spread a sheet across the living room floor inviting about 10 men with dice to come by, using words like, "Jump seven," "Yo eleven," "If she winks, she'll fuck," "Bet 10 or fo'," "I hit 10," "I side bet for twenty," "Bet you don't cum," all kinds of sayings that I didn't understand at the time. But I tell you, as a young man growing up, I would use those words well, and I do mean well.

My Mother. On the other hand, my mother let me join the Boy Scouts with my best friends. That was a great experience for me. It opened my eyes to many things from camping, hiking, cooking, tying knots, archery, to fishing. These are things I would never have experienced otherwise. I also played Pop Warner Football. I remember my first week at practice. Boy, I was nervous. C'mon don't act like you weren't nervous your first time playing a sport. But like I

Moms Get Beat

said, I was nervous. Shit, I started when I was about 13, at 5 feet even, weighing only 84 pounds. All the other boys had been playing since maybe 7 so they knew the game. Outside of watching football with my dad and playing on the weekends in front of the house, I knew nothing about the game. I made it through the first week. Over the next few weeks we practiced for our first game. I remember we had a little practice on Friday and after practice were told to get up, eat breakfast and be ready for our first game in the morning. All night I thought, "Yeah, tomorrow is the big day!" When tomorrow came, moms and pops were all hyped up. Pops chanted, "My man, my little man!" Moms cheered, "That's my son right there!" And it was a big day- a big day to find out how sorry my little ass was. I rode the shit out that bench. To this day I couldn't tell you what pops said, but I will always remember my mama telling me, "Boy I don't come to see you sit yo' ass on the bench! You better take yo' ass to practice and act like you know how to play because if I come again and you sit on the bench, I won't be at another game!" In my head I said, "Mom, most of these dudes' parents are the coaches, so no matter what I do, I won't play."

Man, I went to practice that Monday. They played me as middle line backer and one of the best guys on the team was lined up at running back. He came through the hole and I thought, "Oh shit!" At that moment all I could hear was my mom's voice repeating, "Boy I don't come to see you sit yo'

Chapter 1

ass on the bench! ..." I hit homeboy so hard. I picked him up and slammed his ass. I heard, "Oooohhh!" from the rest of the team. So, from that moment, that one hit, I would start every game and was known as "that little dude who got heart and can hit."

Throughout junior high school I ran track and broke records. No matter what sport I played I was always the smallest on the team. But with what my dad taught me and what my mom said to me, I would always be one of the best on the team.

Junior high school would be the beginning of what would influence criminal behavior in my life. Even though I grew up around violence, it was always violence from other people. I was shocked to see kids my age doing what I thought only older people did. I remember seeing dudes gang-bangin', shootin' dice, smokin' weed and cigarettes, drinkin', and touchin' girls on their butts. "Some of this shit is cool, but some of it I will never do," I thought. But man, the gambling and girls lit a fire under me that I could not wait to put out. So by the 7th grade, we went out chilin', just doing things that we did in junior high school. I met this lil' young broad named Thea. I popped her on the ass and she really didn't say too much so I thought, "Oh shit, this kinda cool!" Thea and I went dippin' into the bathroom humpin' on each other, and shit, every day. I just accidentally slipped my dick in one day and my mind spun, "Ooh shit, I just entered another

Moms Get Beat

mothafuckin' world." Wet and gushy, man. That shit was kind of cool. I was a good student, like I said, but I also told you this was the beginning of my behavior for a criminal mothafuckin' mind. It started with my first taste of pussy. I didn't eat the pussy yet, but I damn sho' fucked the shit out of it.

I was ditchin' school, fuckin', shootin' dice, doing all kinds of shit. I couldn't ditch too hard, with a moms and pops that would still fuck me up. So I played that shit kinda cool, you know. I kept my grades up, but I was really fucking up. The principal and teachers always gave me a pass. I'm ditching but they didn't put that shit on my report card. My first report card didn't show one absent day. I thought, "Oh shit, this really good."

My daily schedule consisted of hanging out in class, shootin' dice in the halls, shootin' dice behind the gym. I got caught but they didn't do shit. That's how junior high school in Compton goes, man. I was running track at school, getting' kinda popular. The little gang bangin' niggas, were out there bangin' so they still got most of the hoes. I didn't bang, but I was doin' my thing on the side, hustlin' I was grabbing the little broads nobody wanted. They were hangin' out at New Way market shopping center in Compton. Niggas were scrappin' every day after school, fighting and all kinds of shit. I did my best to get my ass on home.

Chapter 1

8th grade, 9th grade came and went. There were always those couple of mothafuckas who wanted to test me. I was in class and this bitch ass nigga named William kept fuckin' with me all week. I asked him to, "Go on, go on", but he just kept fuckin' with me. So, one day, this mothafucka decided he wanted to jump fresh in front of the class and pushed my ass over about three or four rows of desks. Like those two boys following me in elementary school, I didn't know what the fuck he did that for. My instinct kicked in, and I did what I learned back in the day- whipped his little Mothafuckin' ass right in class.

That incident improved my scrap 'em skills reputation, so now my chest was out. I was still a little nigga', a REAL LITTLE nigga no bigger than 100 pounds with a lot of heart. I was being tested left and right by other niggas after that. I got into three, four fights. I knocked out a couple of niggas, so now my reputation took me on through high school.

At Dominguez High school in Compton, also known as D High, things were going kinda cool. I had a few little broads. I was still shootin' dice at the back of the school, still hustlin'. I wasn't sellin' dope like some of the other niggas. My basic thing was shootin' dice, going up to AM-PM mini mart/gas station, buying about $50 worth of candy, bringing that shit back to school, and selling it.

I want you to follow me. This is how it all went down in my ambitious mind. A mothafucka didn't want to go to school.

Moms Get Beat

I was making $100 a day in high school sellin' candy. Hey that's good money.

I got a job at the liquor store when I was in the 10th grade. I worked the cash register. What the fuck do you think a nigga out of Compton, at 15, working at a mothafuckin' liquor store, working the mothafuckin' cash register is going to do? I sat there playing hangman and shit. I started sliding dubs to the side for each sale, while playing hangman. Every time the liquor store owners made $100 I made $20. Ambition quickly turned criminal. A complete hangman was worth $100. So, I was making $100 a day at school shooting dice, $100 selling candy, and getting' the liquor store for damn near $50-100 a night. 10th grade nigga was making $600-1000 a week. I really thought I was doing something.

Moms and pops didn't know what was going on. I had my little scooter, playing it quiet. I was up at the skating rink at that time, doing all kind of shit. That was my thing - mothafucka hard on them wheels. I cracked a bitch one night at the skating rink and she was ready to give me some pussy. The best I could do was to tell her to get on the back of my Elite. She snapped with the attitude, "Man, I ain't riding on the back of no fucking scooter!" That was it. I realized, "Fuck, man. It's time to get me a car. I can't put no bitches on the back of my mothafuckin' Elite." I had a little cheese so, I busted this El Camino. I bought it for $1200. Daytons were in at the time, but I didn't get any. I threw on some

Chapter 1

Centerline rims with the holes on it instead. This was 1986. Niggas were drivin' Benzes, Nissan trucks with rims, BMWs, Suzukis, mothafuckin' El Caminos with the SS front end. Everybody had Daytons or Lorenzas, a Benz or Daytons. Now I was on fuckin' Centerlines and shit, so I wasn't getting much pub. It was good for a few little hoes, the ones that weren't trippin'. I wasn't gettin' the bad bitches yet, the 'TOP NOTCH hoes' as other niggas would call 'em. But I did get some bad little ghetto bitches. A mothafucka was getting pussy, and that's all that mattered back then. Long as a nigga got his dick wet.

Back at the liquor store. The cats outside were selling rocks, and they had the balloons. I didn't know what balloons were for at that time. All I heard was mothafuckas asking, "Hey, dawg. You wanna get these balloons? I'll give you some money if you pass these to these guys." I wasn't sellin' any dope, and didn't ever wanna sell dope. I wanted to finish school, and make some shit happen. I was learning the game without knowing it. I watched cats slang rocks on a small scale. My ambitious criminal mind thought, "Mothafuckas are stupid. They are sitting out here in the parking lot selling dope. Why don't they do this shit a different way."

Back in the day, in Compton, there were the Santa Fe Mafia off of Alondra and Santa Fe, and Santana block. Them niggas had it going on back then. Those were the two downest hoods in Compton in the late 80's, early 90's. They

10

were puttin' it DOWN. These mothafuckas were making real cheese. So, speeding you up to the part, this is how things were going in my mind: I was working at the liquor store in the 10th grade. Eleventh grade passed, and I was pretty much doing the same thing; hustlin', selling' candy, shootin' dice, gettin' em' at the liquor store. I was stacking my cheese.

Twelfth grade came along and I entered a whole 'nother game. Bowling became the thing. In '87, '88 we used to hit Cal Bowl like a mothafucka. The niggas up at Cal Bowl had CHEESE. When I say cheese, I know cats that were making $100,000 a week. They gambled $20,000 a game! As a young nigga, I thought, "Oooh shit! If I could just get a piece of this!!!" A mothafucka's dick was hard watching these mothafuckas hit like $20,000 a game. I bowled too, making my little money, more like $500 a game. My homie James and I had game.

One night after getting off work at the liquor store I was with my homeboy Big Mike. We were at Long Beach and Alondra trying to crack some hoes at Taco Bell. Two little bitches rode by and my homeboy said, "Man, them broads is bad, right there. You need to go catch them." So, I sped up and peeped. The driver had long ass hair. I pulled them over, thinking, "Whoooo shit!" I walked up to the car, nervous and shit. I didn't know what to say. All I saw was long silky black hair going down behind the seat. "Ooh!" She turned around and was bad as mothafucka. The gap between her

11

Chapter 1

teeth and freckles were even cute. But man, when I tell you bad. I asked her for her name and we exchange numbers. "Deborah," she said. I told my homeboy, "Man, if this girl gave me the right number, she gon' be my wife one day." I couldn't wait to get home to call her... I couldn't wait.

I got home, called her, and talked to her for a minute. All week I waited for her to call me back. She didn't.

I was still out working. By this time I was at Sinclair Pipeline Company in Compton. I still wasn't trying to get in this dope game, y'all. But after a mothafucka met Deborah, things changed. Now I was trying to keep up with her, take her out, but it was hard. I was trying to do it right. I enrolled in electrical school. I was going to school and working. Things were cool while I was still at home with pops and moms.

Since I quit the liquor store, and graduated high school, I went from making damn near $700-1000 a week to making $6.00 an hour. That's a big ass mothafuckin' difference. I wasn't making SHIT...NOTHING! I started bowling scared since I really couldn't lose any money and needed to start saving.

McDonnell Douglas started hiring, so I went down there and took the test. I passed it and got the job there paying $9.00 an hour. Things were going kinda cool while a mothafucka was trying to figure out how I was gonna make some   more   money.

Chapter 2

Just Got Beat for a Key

"I really don't know what I'm gonna do. I'm trying keep her, I'm trying shoot dice, I'm trying to do all this shit and I just hit a slump one year."

Now mind you the game was still in my face, waiting for me. This shit was hovering over my head since I graduated in mothafuckin' 1988. And this is 1990. The game is just hovering, "Hey, come here. Get in. Come here. Get in." I didn't wanna get in. My sister met her husband, and this mothafucka was ballin'. I watched this mothafucka come pick her up. He came through with the Benz, with the rag top, blue, electric top. Mothafuckas didn't have that shit, so it was enticing me. "Nah, man, I can not do this shit. I'm a good

Chapter 2

boy!" But this shit was in my blood- It was in my blood. My daddy didn't do it but he hustled his mothafuckin' ass off.

I was at McDonnell Douglas tryin' to make it happen. Deborah and I started going through little problems but we were still cool. This was 1990 and I worked there about a year. This was my first contact with mothafuckin' Asians, Chinese, and Japanese, all of that shit. I became real cool with an Asian homeboy named Mike. Now Mike, he got the sack, he was moving weed. He kept spittin' at me like "Kevin, I'm telling you dawg, just do this shit. You can't get in trouble." He was selling weed at McDonnell Douglas and making a killing; $25 sacks; $50 sacks. He came at me again with, "Man, look dawg, I'm gonna give you an ounce. I'm gonna show you what to do." I figured, "This shit ain't cocaine. It's not that bad."

So why the fuck did I start selling some mothafuckin' weed?

Hustling is in my blood. This is when I entered the mothafuckin' game. He fronted me a sack, an ounce, and I broke that shit down into grams. "This shit isn't that bad," I thought. Remember I lived in Compton, the South Side. There were a gang of mothafuckin' weed heads over there. Still are. So I went through the hood telling everybody I got sacks. They laughed at me, and shit. "Nigga you don't even know what the fuck you doing. Get outta here." So, fuck it, he gave me an ounce, I started passing the shit out, giving it to them. Mothafuckas was like, "Damn, this shit is good!"

Now I just paid Mike outta my check after I gave that shit away. Mothafuckas thought I was playin'. They played me like I was some little bitch ass, sucka ass nigga, like I didn't know what the fuck I was doing. So, fuck it. I thought I'd act like I was ballin', but broke as a mothafucka. I gave sacks away, not knowing what I was doin'. I just didn't want niggas calling me stupid. I was slowly building a clientele, without being aware of it. I was sucking mothafuckas in, giving them my product. They were coming at me with, "You got some more of that shit?" Mike hit me with another sack. This time I sold it. This shit was gettin' cool now.

It was '91 at the time. My girl Deborah and I had a son. All kinds of shit happened in '90-91. My girl and I had problems. But I had the sack. It went from an ounce a week to two ounces a week, to three ounces a week. Mothafuckas started asking me if they could buy ounces.

I was fronted a pound for $3,000.00. Half pounds sold for $3,200.00, quarter pounds for $1,700.00, and I was still sellin' my own sacks at $20.00 a gram and $450.00 an ounce. I broke it down, moving three pounds of weed a mothafuckin' week. I was stuck. I was now IN the game at 21.

Chapter 2

Three pounds of mothafuckin' weed a week, broke down into $5.00, $10.00, $20.00, $50.00, $100.00 sacks, ounces, quarter pounds, pounds.

Mothafuckas's coming.

One day my homeboy Doug got at me, "Hey, can you get four pounds of this shit?" My brother-in-law, out there in the game, got at me the same day, "Can you get me four or five pounds?" I told both of them I wasn't sure. "Hey Mike, I got two cat's that wanna get 4 pounds of weed each. You got it?" I sold 8 pounds of weed in a day, so he turned me on to the mothafucka. Mike said, "Oh shit, you doing it like this?" I wasn't doin' it LIKE THIS. I was selling three pounds of weed, but I wasn't sellin' eight at a time. I lied and said, "Yeah, I'm doin it like this," because I was learnin' the game, learnin' how to play this shit. So he trusted me enough to front me the shit, as much as I wanted.

"Nigga, I got pounds of weed, 10 pounds, 20 pounds, 30 pounds whatever you want nigga, I got it." I was getting cocky now, thinking I was the man and shit.

Mike then took me to yet another level.

"Yo, Kevin, man. You kind of a cool, nigga. I got yo back. Your people need some heat?"

"I don't know. I'll put it out there."

I started telling niggas, "I got glocks, I got 9's I got Reugers, I got 38's, I got oozies. Whatever y'all need." It was stupid cuz a mothafucka will go to jail for this shit. But I

Just Got Beat for a Key

wasn't trippin. A mothafucka was hustling. All I saw was the dollar mothafuckin' signs. *Dollar mothafuckin' signs.* I was blinded like a mothafucka. So, here my stupid ass was, selling glocks, oozies and all kinds of mothafuckin' heat.

I remember one day, my homeboy got cracked. My pops was cool with the law. They were kinda friends. So one cop slid up under my brother and said, "Hey, Hawkins. You know, tell yo' little brother to kick back. Somebody just got caught with a heater and told us they got it from y'all." So he hit me and I was like, "Oh shit!" I knew that was serious, so I kicked back from sellin guns. But I still kept my plug, still sold my weed.

Things were still cool. Mothafucka just out there chillin', having a ball, staying low key. But how low key can you stay when you movin' that kind of weed?

There is a whole other side of the game that I'm getting ready to take y'all on, but y'all gotta follow me.

Now mind you, I had a girl, a son, so I really wasn't wild. I was kinda cool, stackin' my chips, going to work, going home to my girl. McDonnell Douglas started laying people off.

"What the fuck am I'm gonna do?"

Here I was again, stuck in a mothafuckin' dilemma. I was trying to stick to marijuana, and not sell dope. I wasn't trying to sell that mothafuckin' white shit, that cocaine... But each time, the thought hovered over my mothafuckin' head.

17

Chapter 2

But, fuck it, McDonnell Douglas was laying off, so what I did I do? I went off on disability.

In '92, I was in the streets all day. I wasn't at work anymore for 8 to 12 hours a day. I met a couple of other bitches outside of my woman. I was fucking broads, getting my dick sucked. That shit was great 'cause my girl really wasn't with that shit. I was still going to the skating rink, going to the bowlin' alley. I was younger than most cats there so I wasn't on their level. My younger brother met this little esè named David. David told him he was gonna hit him with some work, didn't have to give him anything up front, and he could get as much as he wanted. His price was $11,000 when cocaine was going for $13,000. That's $2,000 below the market value.

"Fuck it."

There I was again, telling mothafuckas I got work, I got birds. I hadn't sold a bird yet but I was hittin' everybody I knew- older niggas' brother-in-law, young niggas, whoever in the game.

"Nigga, I got BIRDS."

"Nigga you don't even know what a bird look like," testing my ego again like they did with the mothafuckin' weed. I went to one of my homeboys, "Hey dawg, check this out, take this do whatever you wanna do with it and come holla at me later." I got rid of my first bird. I fronted him, but

18

Just Got Beat for a Key

I got my own money to back it up. I had $13,000 so if something went down I could cover that. He came back; they tell him the shit was good. Now he asked me if I could get 5 of 'em. Shit in my lap again! I told my little brother to go holla back at David... So we did it. Now we were out here, moving a little weight. Mothafuckas were saying, "K got the birds, Kevin and his brother got work."

Here we go. I fucked with these niggas up outta Watts not really knowin' the game. I hadn't checked the package, so I couldn't tell you what this shit looked like. I just knew it was white. They came back, "Hey Kevin check this out, man. We opened this package and they got this white shit sitting on top of some brown shit." I didn't know what was really going on. So I holla'd at my esès, "Y'all just beat me. I just sold this shit to some niggas and they knockin' at my door. What's goin' on?"

"Keeny Keeny we no do that!" Those mothafuckas done played me. Now I got niggas like, "Hey you owe us." I know I owe these mothafuckas so what was I gonna do? I holla'd at my brother-in-law. He told me to hold up to my end. I holla'd at my brothers they told me to hold up. So these niggas were trying to push up. I told them, "You know what dawg, check this out. Y'all didn't check it, I didn't check it, so we gon' split this." I gave it to 'em for $16,500.00 so I had to come up with $8,250.00. So I gave em that, but they kept trying push up like I was some soft ass nigga, for the rest of the

19

Chapter 2

money. I let em know, "It ain't that type of party homie, I ain't gonna give you nothing else." We let that shit fade out. That's how I get beat for my first key.

From that day forward I made sure I cut a BIG ASS triangle out the top, a BIG ASS triangle out the bottom and a BIG ASS triangle out the side. I checked all of this shit, every time, to make sure a mothafucka don't beat me.

I ain't losing no more work, I ain't losing shit!

Chapter 3

Two Hundred Thousand Dollars in a Week

A year of this shit went by. I went back and forth moving one, two or three. Then a drought season hit. This time I made 3 or 4 other connections with some esès. I played them. They were all giving me work at $10,000 and $11,000 a key and wasn't shit moving for under $13,000 to the streets. I was getting them, at $2,000 under, each one. The shit started taking off. My brother-in-law started fucking with me, getting 5 and 10 keys at a time. I had niggas from Watts coming to get 10 at a time. I had niggas from LA coming to

21

get 5. I had homies going to Arkansas, New Orleans, New York, Ohio, Detroit, Chicago. Man, I had cats from everywhere coming to get work. So when the drought season hit, a mothafucka moved a gang of work. In a week, I moved 100 keys. "Ooh shit, two thousand dollars a pop! "DAMN!" It was fucking '92, I was 22, and this time a mothafucka was out here. I was on one, I'm telling you.

I started going to clubs, hangin' out, pulling up at the bowlin' alley, shooting dice, wildin' out. A nigga just hit **$200,000 in a week...** "WHAT, WHAT, WHAT!! I'm a young nigga, I'm out here now, I'm in this shit, I'm in the game!" Imagine hitting a lick for $200,000.00 in a week. Now this shit was crazy to me. I was at home, laying up in the bed, my girl sleepin' next to me. My head was spinning as I played back over my life.

All I could think about was the birth of my son. I had my son on November 6, 1990. At that time the world was in a crazy place. All I thought about doing was working and being a good dad. I wasn't corrupt, I didn't sell drugs. I was basically just working, shooting dice, you know, going through the typical shit in my relationship.

I had a daughter on May 6, 1992. With a son and a daughter now, a mothafucka really didn't want to be a mothafuckin' drug dealer. I just slipped up in this shit. But now, I'm tweaking cuz I just hit 'em for like $200,000.00 in a week and I didn't know what the fuck to do. I still had my

Two Hundred Thousand Dollars in a Week

job, I didn't quit, I was on disability. And on top of all that shit, I was in the game! This is what I was telling myself. "You in the game. You a mothafuckin' dope dealer now. When you sellin' weed, that shit ain't nothing. But to sell a hundred keys in a week? What the fuck?!" That was some unimaginable shit for a street level nigga.

And that's what I'm talking about, that street level shit.

I wasn't a nigga bringing crates of fucking drugs and shit from Columbia. This was a street level nigga that got a plug between some esès and me. Imagine a mothafucka moving work like that.

So I was layin' in this bed and I'm FUCKED UP!!!! I just made $200,000.00 in a week I already had some change stacked from selling weed. I could quit, but if I quit I didn't have a college education. A nigga was straight up outta high school, 22. Everybody around me was selling dope. Part of my conscience was telling me, "You can quit now, homie." So I laid there for hours, all kind of shit going through my head.

"I can't be doing this with my kids or my girl up in this house. We are already having problems."

So I started thinking I had to get another place, move my family out. I'm bugged out, dawg. I'm telling you, I'm bugged out. I went to sleep and slept pretty good.

Chapter 3

The next morning my phone was blowing up, my pager was blowing up and I was out here tweakin'. I was just out on the streets didn't know where to go. Mothafuckas were calling me, "That shit is bomb." "Nigga, can you get me 10?" I had niggas calling me from everywhere and all I was doing now was moving work. I stayed low key in a '92 Honda Wagon on some 18 inch Azevs while everybody else was driving Lexo's.

I kept hittin' clubs. I hit this one club called the China club and that shit was cracking. All this shit that I was doing, with all these stupid bitches. They were sucking my dick. That shit wasn't really being done with me and my girl. Sex was a big issue with us. Mothafucka know he's good. But she's just like "I'm not into that shit." So when she do it, she's half ass doing it.

Chapter 4

My Homie Got Jacked for His Car

At 22 with money, I was pulling some amazing bitches. One night my homeboys and I stepped up in a strip club in Bellflower called Fritz. This was my first taste of a strip club. As soon as I walk up in that mothafucka, dawg.... WHOOO!!! All I can tell you is "OH MY MOTHAFUCKIN' GOD!!!" I saw some of the baddest white bitches and sistas I had ever seen. I got my first table dance, twenty dollars a pop. A nigga had money so I let her give me 10 dances. I wasn't tripping. I was making cheese out here.

Chapter 4

So I got the little table dance, and she danced for me. I just gave this bitch $200.00 and I ain't got shit outta this. I was at these clubs 2 or 3 nights a week. As I was in there, I was really learning the game, seeing how it went. I was watching other cats. I just start hollering at these broads, "What's up? What is it gonna take for a nigga to get you up outta here and get a private dance?" Morgan was bad and I was ON HER. I went up to her.

"What's up, I'm up in here fucking with you, you getting $100, $200 a pop, I ain't trying stay up in here. I need a private dance."

"You crazy!"

"I'm just saying, we done got to know each other by now so, what's up?"

"Look, Kevin. Check this out. I'll meet you for lunch one day if that's cool."

So she told me to meet her at this spot in Brea off the 57. I met her there and we had a nice little lunch. This bitch is really bad. I usually saw her in the strip club under lights but when I saw her in the day time, "Shit!" All I can tell you is "she was BAD". Brown-skinned, caramel, nice curly good hair, brown eyes, nice firm ass and titties. My scene was Compton, LA, Watts, Cerritos and Lynwood. But the clubs I was going to were out in Hollywood and they cool but when you into the strip club scene, in '92, you talking a whole nother level. They ain't fucking with these broads in the strip

My Homie Got Jacked for His Car

club 'cause they in there getting they paper so they gotta be top notch. So after I meet her for lunch, everything is cool. We hook up, it took about another week. She took off them clothes and a mothafucka was just like "Ooh am I really finna get this? Am I really finna go up in this" This bitch got me going. The head she gave me....whooooooooo!!!! How she rode a mothafucka!!! Now remember I told you, I'm having problems at home already. So I'm like fuck it, so I stay I hit, I'm out late and we chillin'.

By this time, my girl, my kids, and I lived together. We had a nice 3 bedroom house, upstairs/downstairs, two houses down from moms and pops. One day, walking down the stairs, this bitch threw a big ass 4 pound jug of Vaseline at me. It hit me in the middle of my fucking back. I tried to catch that shit and I missed it. Lord knows if I woulda caught it, I woulda fucked her ass up. You already know Pops whooped on Moms, so that shit wasn't really in me to hit a woman. I could have walked up them stairs and beat the dog shit outta her at that moment. But I didn't. I looked up, with tears in my eyes, my son at the bottom of the stairs, "Man, Daddy loves you." I walked down the stairs and out the door.

I walked straight down to moms and pops. Pops asked, "What's wrong son?"

"Dad, me and Debra done got into it."

"What y'all get into about?"

Chapter 4

"The shit already been going bad, pops. But I been out in these streets. I ain't really been at home because I ain't feeling this relationship. I love my kids but I ain't really feeling this. So I tell her I'm getting ready to go out, she threw a can and hit me in the back."

I stayed there for a minute with pops, we chopped it up. I got a phone call from Q, this little broad I cracked who did hair. She was a fly little broad. We had been fucking around back and forth but I hadn't really hit yet. I was still mad, so I thought, "Fuck it." We went out and got dinner in West Covina. There was a hotel out there. She had a dude. He was blowin' her up. My girl was blowin' me up. I didn't want to fuck with her at all tonight, so I left my phone in the car. I had been fucking around, but I was home every night. This night was one night a nigga wasn't coming home. So I said to Q, "What's up, we gonna get this room?"

"I ain't tripping, I ain't got nobody to answer to, my nigga don't run me."

"Shit, it's on and crackin' 'cause my bitch don't run me neither."

So we got a room at the hotel. You know a mothafucka like pussy. A mothafucka done turned out to be a hell of a pussy eater too. On top of fucking these bitches a nigga can eat the shit out of some mothafuckin' pussy. I mean that's the thang. I love it. I like it. I'ma eat it. You know, it's like a mothafuckin' envelope, you lick it before you mothafuckin'

28

stick it. Once you lick it, you put that stamp on that bitch and you seal it and send it off 'cause it's ready to be delivered.

The night went on and we freaked the whole time. A nigga fell asleep that night like she was my broad. It was about 7:30a.m. When I woke up, she woke up. We like, "Shit, the morning done caught us."

When I got home, my girl was sitting up in the bed, mad as a mothafucka. The look in my eyes told her I really didn't give a fuck because I really didn't.

"I'm tired of this shit, Kevin. You're not going to just keep disrespecting me."

"Check this out. Whatever you do, you do!"

"I don't wanna be here."

"Look, check this out. I'll tell you what." (Now in my mind I'm already thinking I gotta buy another spot because I can't be selling dope with my kids in the house. It's too dangerous. A mothafucka's name ain't really ringing, but people who know me know I got mad work.)

You go find you a place, and when you do, let me know how much you need."

So she bounced. She come back later on that day and said she found a place. She said she needed $3,000.00.

"That's it? Here you go. You need furniture? Here you go."

I furnished my kids' rooms, her room, the living room, dining room. I didn't care, 'cause that was my way out. She

29

Chapter 4

bounced for good, and a mothafucka was like, "Oh shit it's on and cracking."

We moved in the current place in 1990 when I was working and didn't have money, so the place was full of some bull shit ass furniture, like from the furniture stores always going out of business, on the corners. It wasn't even my taste. So, I refurnished my shit the way I wanted it. I got some new furniture and pimped my shit out like a mothafucka. I was out there now, my girl gone, my kids gone. I didn't have shit holding me back. Nobody knew where they lived so I was really just out here.

It was late '92. She moved, but I was still fuckin' with her. I was fucking with broads in the street and I had a key to the place. I was living the life. I could fuck with her, fuck with my bitches in the street, hustle. Nobody knew where she lived or where I was so I was kinda like a ghost on these streets.

I felt the heat coming because a couple of mothafuckas were getting' kinda salty, and greedy. One morning, I got a knock at the door. Some mothafuckin' esè that I hadn't ever seen before in my life asked if I was Kevin. I had bars and shit on the door, so I didn't open it. I had my dogs, rotts, and pits that I trained. I slid out the back, came around with my dogs and said, "What's up. I'm Kevin. What's up?" We stood there looking at each other for minute. I had my heat. Black Talon hollow-points in all my guns, a Smith & Wesson

30

My Homie Got Jacked for His Car

snubbed nosed 38, a mothafuckin' Berretta 9mm with a 30 round clip with the infrared. Since I came around the side of my house they really didn't say anything. I guess the shit didn't quite go as planned. So they walked out the gate.

I had mothafuckas watching me. This life was really becoming my reality. I was a drug dealer. I wasn't born in this shit, nor was I raised with the intentions on being a mothafuckin' drug dealer. I still had a "good God" mentality. But my father was a hustler, so I was raised around this shit. All my homeboys were in this shit, so I wasn't stupid or blind. I wasn't oblivious to this shit. I had to start watching my back.

Remember I told you about my homeboy James? Now we were raised together. Since he lost his job, he was just in the hood kickin' it. He was getting' high and drunk everyday. He peeped the esès at my house. After they left, I put my Rottweiler named Diablo and my pit-bull named Sasha, up. I had Mustafa, another pit, with me. I walked across the street to talk to James.

"Dawg, what's up man? What's up homie? Nigga, you out here. You ain't working; you ain't doing shit, man. I can't see you like this. I always told you if one of us make it we gonna help the other one out. I got my shit going, I see you watchin'. I know you looking. So, this is what we gonna do. Check this out. Stop getting' high in the daytime. I ain't telling you to stop completely. Stop drinking in the day time

Chapter 4

and I'ma fuck with you. I guarantee you that you gonna be alright. Don't even trip. But you gotta leave this shit alone. I don't know what you doing, but you always high and drunk, and you can't function like that. Nigga, this game out here is kinda wicked. You and I both know that shit."

James agreed, "I can do that!" So he cleaned himself up.

Now I wasn't gonna hit him with a sack, but what I planned to do was teach him the game and pull him in up under me. So what I did, if I made $2,000.00 he made $1,000. Whatever I made, he made half. That's how I was doing this shit 'cause that was my nigga. I already stacked a nice amount of change, so fuck it. "I'ma take care of my nigga."

I told him, "Hey, dawg. You gotta keep this shit on the hush. You can't let mothafuckas know 'cause its kinda wild out here." I pull my homie in the game.

We were movin' an average of about 5 keys a day, or 30 keys a week. We never moved under 25 keys a week. The max would be 60-70 depending on how a mothafucka felt. A nice 6 months went by and James stacked some nice paper. He started back drinking so I had to stop fuckin' with him 'cause it was gettin' wild.

I still had my Asian partners, givin' me the real work, half-ass fuckin' with weed. My Asians done turned me on to this other game. Counterfeit money. They were printin' hundreds of thousands of this shit. I saw another opportunity, so I started fuckin' with them. I already had my cats going out of town buying work, comin' in buying work. I had my cats off of Santa Fe buying work. I had a lot of different niggas buying work. So I started gettin' at these cats.

"Hey, I got this counterfeit money. I'll sell y'all $20,000 for $5,000."

I started moving hundreds of thousands of this shit. I spread my house, the whole floor, from the living room, dining room, den, to the kitchen, with counterfeit money in order to bleach it with a spray that would imitate the texture of a true bill. Man, I was selling so much counterfeit money so fast. It was too easy to get into too many hustles at one time. The risk was, having too many niggas in yo business. I decided to cut out the counterfeit money hustle and stick to the work.

By this time, James fell completely out of the game. I tried to convince him that I needed somebody to fuck with. I trusted him.

"Just stop drinking man. Just stop! Get off this shit and get yo' money! You can get drunk at night when you done with this shit."

"You know what? You right."

So he left the shit alone a second time. We were rollin' into summer of '93. James and I came up together, but we were different. My homie liked low riders and shit so he went and bust this clean ass mothafuckin' Cadillac. This mothafuckin' 'lac- when I tell you it was clean...man, it was

33

Chapter 4

clean. For a new cat to get into the low riding game, he did it right.

We had a car wash back in the day on Long Beach Boulevard and Alondra. We were up there chillin' and my homeboy hopped out the 'lac to get some cigarettes at the gas station on the side of the car wash. While inside, some fools hopped in his shit and drove off in it.

"Kevin, nigga! They just grabbed my shit!"

"What! What?"

He hopped in our homeboy's car at the car wash. I went to the house, about two to three blocks away, to get my fully automatic oozie with the hundred round clip in it. My other homeboy and I hopped in another car. We went flying through mothafuckin' Compton, down Long Beach Boulevard, hit Rosecrans. I was on the phone with him. They were heading down Alameda. We were flyin' down Alameda chasin' these niggas. I was flyin' runnin' lights, hittin' corners with a fully automatic ooze in my shit with a hundred round clip. Imagine what the fuck would have happened if the police had pulled us over. IMAGINE THAT! 22 year old, with a hundred round clip, fully automatic oozie, with a trigger job. I was thinking, "I ain't stupid." But I wasn't givin' a fuck 'cause these niggas just got my homie. They just went up in the Pueblos. The Pueblos are niggas, worse than mothafuckin' Watts. That shit's worse than the Nickerson's 'cause there were a gang of esès up in there.

My Homie Got Jacked for His Car

"What you wanna do, James? I ain't trippin, nigga we can go up in this mothafucka if that's what you wanna do."

"Man, it ain't worth it."

"Well, that's yo call, nigga. I got yo back. If I need some more heat don't worry. Don't even trip, nigga. I got whatever you need. I ain't playin, nigga. I am not playin' out here."

"Naw, man, fuck it."

"Alright fuck it. It ain't my shit. That's yo shit."

We turned around and left. That was a typical day in the hood, right there. That's how that shit went. That's just how shit was going in my life. When I say shit was kinda getting crazy, it was getting wild.

I had another homeboy, Mel. He's one of the niggas that bought some of the first work from me. He was out in Indiana tearin' their ass up. He was fuckin' with niggas with real paper. He always gave me his paper the day before in fresh hundreds. I liked fuckin' with his folks. They generated $180,000.00 income for me. You don't really see niggas with fresh hundreds comin' from the bank. That usually means they either have a legitimate business somewhere or they're going to the bank to turn over the cash. Most niggas that were sellin' dope out in the streets would give me $3,000.00 worth of ones, $40,000 in fives, tens and twenties all dirty and shit. I had to sit and count all this shit. I didn't own a money counter. I was already doing wrong, and a money counter added almost 5 years more if you ever got caught

35

with dope. I was sittin' up here countin' this shit myself. By the time I finished it was late.

I was layin' up in the bed again one night. The same thought lingered, "I gotta do something with this money and this life. This shit ain't me, man. This shit ain't me!" But it was hard to quit. I didn't want to walk away from the kind of money I had been getting'. I was thinking that maybe if I did something else, I might be able to get up out the game.

I had another partner named Craig. He was rappin' and shit. I heard him flow one day and I thought this nigga was kinda tight! I had some money, as you know, so I told him, "Yo, dawg. I got some money. I'll get behind y'all and we can fuck with this studio shit." Craig and Russ J, had a group called the Black Sox. We were all at the studio, and they were making music and shit. This music business is a whole different game. I told my homeboy James, "If I ain't around, nigga, you handle the work. You already know the game, you got it well." James was a nigga I could trust, my dawg. His only problem was drinking, but he had that under control since it was about paper right now.

Chapter 5

Tryin' To Get Out the Dope Game

I was hoping I could get into the music game, turn it around, and get out the dope game. But it wasn't movin'. We were doing music but it wasn't movin. I went over to my brother's car wash and looked across the street. The empty building across the street had a "For Lease" sign on it. Coincidentally, I was outside talking to one of my homeboys, Brian, who worked at the bank. I told him, "You know what, Brian? I'm gonna put me a barbecue restaurant right there." I knew how to cook from moms, and how to barbecue from pops. A nigga had skills up in the kitchen. Brian agreed that it was a good idea.

I called the number on the building. The owner said he only wanted around $500 dollars for the lease. I made an appointment to look inside. It was completely empty. Being good at interior decorating, I was cool with it. I'm pretty much a jack of all trades. I ain't MASTERED shit, but a mothafucka is kind of talented. The inside was cool, but the front of the building went into a triangle. I told the guy I didn't like it. He said the owner of the building was into construction so they could pull it out. We agreed that if they removed that triangle, and gave me time to get the building together, I'd take it. He gave me three months to get the building together.

I had money didn't want to spend it, so I got at a few cats and told them I was gonna open up a barbecue restaurant and asked them if they wanted to go in on it. Most weren't interested. So, I got at my brother in law.

"Hey bro you wanna go in with me to put this restaurant right here?"

He wasn't in a position to help. So, "Fuck it."

I had money saved, but I really didn't want to do this shit by myself, but I just start grindin' like a mothafucka. I wasn't passin' shit up.

I had the construction goin' on with the restaurant, I was fuckin' with the music studio, I had shit crackin'. This shit was coming along kinda nice. I thought my life might change. I might be able to stop selling dope. I was starting to feel good about myself.

Tryin' To Get Out The Dope Game

I went up in Fritz one night and this bad bitch named Barbie was up in there. This broad was Cuban and black. I got a dance from her and I fucked with her all night.

Some weeks went by and I was still fuckin' with the studio and the barbecue restaurant. I pick up some books and read about the music business. I invested some money into the Black Sox, and we had maybe 4-5 songs recorded. I learned about contracts to protect myself. My brother Willy, who had been in the business for a while, turned me on to a music attorney. The attorney advised that I start a corporation, so I established one and named it, Yahweh Entertainment. Yahweh is Hebrew for God. It means, "I am who I am. I bring all into existence that is". So, if this is to be, God was going to bring it into existence. I start my company, got the contracts together, we split the company 33⅓%. Brian, who was working at the bank, had a cousin named Steve who worked at E.M.I music publishing. Brian heard about this shit because he and Craig worked at the bank together. Brian thought the group was tight. He took it to his cousin Steve.

Steve gave the group a demo deal, which were popular at the time. Steve didn't really liking the idea of Black Sox, since he wasn't really feeling Russ J. He liked his lyrics, but wasn't feeling him. So he told Craig he wanted to try to get him a deal. We worked on this deal with E.M.I. Music Publishing for Craig. The plan was to get Craig signed, then bring Russ in later. Russ agreed.

Chapter 5

August 1993. My restaurant was coming up. I put a big balloon on top that said, "Hole in the Wall Barbecue Coming Soon". Hole in the Wall was the perfect name because the place was only about 600 square feet. Our promotions went on through construction. We were about a month from opening up. Everything was happening so fast. Everyone, I got at before, was trying to get in touch with me, to get in on it, now. After I done grinded like this? I was cool. I spent a nice amount of change without them. I didn't need them now.

The only exception was my brother-in-law. Being family, I let him in. I had about $90,000.00 invested out of my own pocket into this. I put in electrical, plumbing, floors, tables, equipment, everything new, with cash outta my pocket 'cause I wasn't familiar with credit game. Back in the day, I fucked my credit off since I didn't understand it I wasn't trippin' 'cause when you're black, growing up, they tell you, "Don't fuck with credit. It ain't good for you." We were never really educated about it. In the ghetto, if you have cash, you The Man. With cash you can buy whatever you want. So I told my brother-in-law I'd hit him with whatever he wanted and he could slide me my paper later.

The restaurant opened on August 3rd, 1993. I had invested $110,000.00 of my own cash in this. I didn't have to touch any of the money I had saved. I was grindin' like a Mothafucka, movin' about 40 keys a week, so I wasn't giving a fuck.

Tryin' To Get Out The Dope Game

I had a '89 Iroq, convertible; gray, with the Boyed shit all in it, foot pedals, steering wheel. I had sounds all in this bitch and chrome iroqs on it. The mothafucka was sweet! I told Craig that if we got a deal, I would give him that mothafuckin' car. I wasn't trippin'. A nigga had paper. I wasn't even into cars. I had money, and I could get whatever the fuck I wanted. That's how I was rollin', and that's how I was feelin'. If I wanted to go buy a new car, I did that shit.

Craig got super tight in this Mothafuckin' rap game. He got the publishing deal at E.M.I. publishing for $60,000.00. They paid him $30,000 up front until he had acquired a deal, at which time they'd pay the other half. I got my percentage. Shit was goin' well for a mothafucka, and I felt good about myself. I was about to get out this dope game.

I wasn't ready for what happened the day the restaurant opened. There were a few other barbecue restaurants in Compton, but I promoted the fuck out this shit. The day the restaurant opened, the only people working it were my sister Rena, my brother in law Dave, two or three employees, and myself. When the doors opened, I tell you, there was a crowd lined up outside waiting to get in. We could not handle it. My mama, my daddy, my other brother-in-law George, were among the many that had to come up there to help.

I had an idea, but I didn't know one mothafuckin' thing about running a business. All I knew how to do was sell dope,

Chapter 5

'cause I had a hell of a plug. In the dope game, you're only as good as your plug.

We sold a gang of ribs. The first day went crazy. I think we generated about $4,000.00 to 5,000.00 in sales. Not bad for a first day of sales. We ended up running out of meat, out of everything. I had a big ass menu: beef ribs, pork ribs, rib tips, chicken breast sandwiches, roast beef sandwiches, greens, potato salad, baked beans, lemon cake, chocolate cake. I had a hell of a menu. At the end of the day after the restaurant closed, I was thinking that everything was going pretty well, "Thank you Lord!"

I wasn't really into church, but I have an older sister Dee who stayed in my ear about coming to church and going to God. We weren't raised in the church, but we knew of the church, because I had an aunt in the church. My prayer was "Father Lord, in the name of Jesus protect me from these demons out here and keep me safe. Keep your angels around me; don't let anything happen to me." I would get on my knees every night because I knew I wasn't living right. My heart was right, but I wasn't living right. I wasn't right. I knew what I was doing wasn't right because I was raised right. But, by the same token, it wasn't about being raised right because everyone is lost out here. Everyone knows the difference between right and wrong, but right don't mean a mothafuckin' thing when you makin' hundreds of thousands. Mothafuckin' money is right. That's what's right out here.

Tryin' To Get Out The Dope Game

I was still skatin' in 1993. A mothafucka rollin', you know. I was hittin' the skatin' rink, playing at the bowling alley. A mothafucka was still out here having fun in the midst of handling his business. I had the record label CRACKIN', I had the Hole in the Wall Barbecue CRACKIN'. So now I was really feelin' my mothafuckin' self. One night I was up at the skatin' rink and I saw this little yellow broad with short hair. She was probably like 5'6". I thought, "Damn, who is this cute little mothafucka." I done been through the whole skatin' rink, cracked a gang of hoes. But I had never seen her before. I holla'd at her and she gave the number. I had never fucked with a girl with short hair before, but she had a cute little short hair cut. We hit it off at the end of '93 to '94. She was a cool little broad.

One night I came up on a quick $30,000.00 - 40,000.00 so I went up to Fritz 'cause I was feeling good. I was goin up to Fritz to get Barbie. I wanted to get this bitch 'TONIGHT!' I was gonna get that bitch that night. I knew the game by this time. All these bitches had a quota to meet, whether its four or five hundred. I slid her a hundred to give me this dance. I slid her another hundred to come give me this dance. I asked her what she was doing that night. She said she wasn't doing anything, so I since it was slow up in there, I suggested she let me take her home.

"I ain't fuckin with you, Kevin."

"Alright. Fuck it."

Chapter 5

After the club, I normally go and hop on the freeway at Bellflower. I don't know what made me go down to Artesia and get on at Lakewood Boulevard instead, but low and behold, guess who I saw- Barbie. I pulled up in the parking lot and let her know that I needed her to go with me. Gave her $300.00, "Lets roll."

"No."

"Here is $400.00, here is $500.00." I was going to keep on until this bitch said, "Yeah."

"What is it gonna take?"

" $1,000.00."

"You got that, let's roll."

She thought I was playing, but I broke her off a $1,000.00. We got a room in Buena Park off the 91 at Beach Boulevard. Bitches out there that's reading this, and homies, if you ain't a bitch; if you would have seen the body on her you would've been whatever she called you. When she took her clothes off "Oh my God, she had a pussy between her legs, camel toes, apple whatever you wanna call it, the gap was a mothafucka!! I'm like, "Oooh shit." The bitch brought goose bumps all over my body she was so bad. And I'm finna get this shit tonight! When I go up in that shit, it was like silk. I slid up in that shit so nice I was just like, "Oh my God!" I tell you what freaky had to do. I ate this bitch so swell, I ate the lining outta her ass. She was going crazy. We fucked for a while.

Tryin' To Get Out The Dope Game

Back in the day, mothafuckas was making tapes so I brought a tape up in there with me. We went through a ninety minute tape, on the other side, back on the side and on the way back. That's how long we fucked. I broke her down so if you're wondering if it was worth a $1,000.00? (Do bears shit in the woods?) Hell yea, it was worth that and more.

1993, and I was taking $5,000.00 - $10,000.00 to Vegas every mothafuckin' weekend. Let me hip you niggas up to some game. I was moving a gang of work so I had to find a way to put this shit in the bank. I took the $5,000.00 - $10,000.00 immediately go to the crap table and exchanged it for chips. I was gambling $100.00 - $500.00 a roll. I took $5,000.00, made about $8,000.00 plus my $5,000.00. So when I went to the cash cage to collect my money I requested my money in a check. You know what I did with that? I put the $13,000.00 in the bank. That's how I was building my bank account.

I was at the Mirage gambling with my player's Card. Most of the pit bosses knew me, so when I went in the casino they'd say, "Hey there, Mr. Hawkins. How are you doing? How is it going, sir? Do you need anything tonight?" If I were staying the night, I would get a complimentary room or meal.

My girl, Debra, didn't have a car. I had the Honda Accord Wagon on 18's, a clean ass Cutlass, and I still had the Iroq 'cause Craig still didn't get a record deal. I couldn't have my girl out here like this. This cat in the game was tryin' to get at my girl when I first met her. He used to ask her, "Why you fuckin' with this broke nigga?" He had a broad now that frequented the skatin' rink. He was locked up, and I wasn't into hittin niggas bitches while they were jail. Ain't nothing playerish about it. He didn't really like me since I snatched my baby mama from his ass. When the nigga came home, he tried to holla at my girl. Well since he wanted to try to holla at my girl, and his girl was tryin to holla at me, guess what? I saw her at the skatin rink and said, "What's up girl? We need to exchange numbers." So we did. With my reputation at the skatin rink, I hit. Things got real cool between us, and it seemed like she was fallin' for a nigga. I kept it real though, because bitches back then didn't fall for a nigga. We thought they did, but these bitches had game out here just as well. They knew who had the money and they were tryin' to get it.

I liked my little 18 year old. I was just fuckin' all the other little broads. My girl wasn't really rollin, and out in the streets, a nigga can't have his broad lookin' shady. I busted her a white '93 Camry with the rims on it, leather interior with the wood, tail on it, tinted windows. I hooked this mothafucka up at All Star. I paid cash and surprised her for Christmas. While she was asleep I pulled the car in the garage, and put a big ass red bow on it. The next morning she went out to the garage, and was happy as a mothafucka. She had a nigga feeling real playerish.

New Year 's Eve was coming and my girl and I were going to Vegas to bring in the New Year. That's when her game turned shady. I used to keep a billfold on me, with about $3,000.00 in it. I had a stack of $5,000.00 in my pocket. We were at the condo getting dressed and ready to roll. I went to count my money, as I do out of habit everyday, no matter what. The money in my billfold was straight. I went through the roll of $5,000.00 to count that shit and I had $4,900.00. Where'd the hundred go? I knew it was gone because I never miscount money, trust me.

"This bitch done stole a hundred dollars from me."

I asked Deborah if she took $100 out of my pocket. She denied it.

"I had $3,000.00 in my wallet and I had $5,000.00 right here, and you telling me you didn't take no money? Well, let me walk around this house then."

I went from room to room.

"We must have a ghost!"

We tore the room apart and this mothafucka looked up under the bed, "Here go the hundred dollars right here!" like it was funny. I asked her why she would steal from me.

"You ain't gotta steal from me. I give you everything you want."

Chapter 5

We were already on bad terms, and that shit hurt me so, I went off. I still went to Vegas. I wasn't going to let that ruin my weekend. I cared about her since she was the mother of my kids and I hoped it could work, but the shit was just all fucked up.

So I thought I'd go to Vegas, have some fun, come back and do what I do. I was ready to bring in 1994. It was my first time in Vegas during New Years. We were out there in Vegas and we really having a ball until one night a nigga got hit for a quick $3,000.00, then another $2,000.00. I lost $5,000.00 just like that. "Damn!" Then I lost the money in my fuckin' billfold. I used to carry a mailbag because that's where I kept my snub noise 38 pistol. The mailbag had $2,000.00 in it. I didn't know how cats do this shit in Vegas, so a mothafucka clipped me at the crap table at Treasure Island, which had reopened.

I had a few partners staying at my house now who were like family. I called the house and T answered the phone. I told him I needed him to wire $3,000.00 to me.

"I ain't got that!"

"I know you don't. Don't trip. I'm about to tell you where it is".

I used to keep a nice amount of money at my house in Compton, so I would be alright. I didn't keep a lot up in there because niggas were shady. I had a few people that I trusted, so my sister knew were my safe deposit box was. We were the only ones that knew about it, and that's where some of my money was.

T sent the money to me, and Deborah and I enjoyed the rest of our time in Vegas, bringing in 1994 at a nice black tie affair.

Chapter 6

I Gotta Get Out the Hood

The restaurant was doing about $18,000 a month in sales, but a nigga had to work 15-16 hours a day. It was good money, but not enough after being in the game. Shit, sometimes $18,000.00 wasn't even an hours worth of work. I wasn't losing interest in the restaurant, but my focus wasn't there because I was fuckin' with the music industry. I saw the amount of money that could be made. My homeboy Melow and his pops had an independent record label and they were working with Redman. Melow brought him by the restaurant to grab something to eat one day. He ate our food like he had never eaten food like that before. My thoughts went into catering for the music industry. I had catered a party for EMI, Music Publishing once because Steve and Brian always ate at the restaurant and loved the food. But I had never considered trying to do catering in the music industry until Redman came in. I start hanging out in Hollywood going to the night clubs, get affiliated with the life.

January '94, Glam Slam night Club started crackin'. My niggas and I decide to roll up there one night. One of my homeboys was rolling in a Grand National and my other homeboy was in a Lexus. I was in my convertible Iroq. My Iroq couldn't keep up with them on the freeway and my Mothafuckin' male ego kicked in. I was pissed because I knew I had the money to get what I wanted but I never tripped on cars- until that night. I had been eyeballin' a twin turbo Supra for a while, but my brother-in-law, who had been in the game for a while, was keeping me away from cars since he knew what could happen.

"You don't need that shit, make your money and be cool."

"Alright, but the next $40,000 I make, I'm going to buy a Supra."

"Alright."

It just so happened I made the $40,000 within about three days. So the next mothafuckin' week I bought the brand new twin turbo Supra Limited Edition. They ran about $53,000 at

Chapter 6

that time. I took that mothafucka up to Wheel Warehouse in Anaheim and got some 18 inch Anteras and threw em on that mothafucka. When I hit the corner, niggas was biting they teeth like, "Damn, dawg what is it?" Niggas didn't have twin turbos on the streets. Asians knew what it was. Most niggas was rolling Grand Nationals and Lexus' I was tearin' em a new ass!

This is where I fucked up though. A nigga got that whip, and now I looked like dope dealer cause I was too young to be rolling some shit like this. My head was still kinda level but I was fuckin' with too many hoes now. I was hittin' an average of about two different hoes a week.

We hit Roxbury, a new club, one night after we left the studio. Steve, Mel, Craig, my homeboy James and I. We got up to the door in jeans and pollo shirts. We weren't dressed 'cause we was just left the studio doing music. The mothafucka at the door wouldn't let us in.

"Dawg, what's up? You just let Suge, Snoop, Daz and Warren G. in with the same gear."

A gang of Mothafuckas from Death Row got in. I got salty the way they were treating these niggas like God. In my mind I was thinking, "Back in the day, before Snoop came out and you Mothafuckas start sucking his dick, when he was signed to my brother, he was being called whack. Before Suge became the CEO of Death Row, he was in the game fucking with my older brother who was fuckin' with me. But

I Gotta Get Out the Hood

I'm not known to the mothafuckin' industry." But after the door man treated them like God, they were going to know who the fuck we were. We all left to get dressed. We put our best jewels. Steve got the 300CE coupe, white, gray bottom with Lorenzos on it. Mel got the green 850 and I got the Supra. We pulled up like, "Bam, bam, bam!" Gave the valet $300.00

"Keep these mothafuckas up front."

We went to the door.

"Here goes $200.00 for yo pocket. Now can we get in?"

They walked us right past the line, into the club. When we got in the club Mothafuckas were watching. We had on $50,000.00 watches, and jewels for yo ass. Imagine a young nigga, 23. There was a whole different breed of groupie bitches in there. They were different then at the Glam Slam. This Hollywood scene was kinda wild cause these bitches were comin' in their best costumes- shoes and dresses they couldn't afford. All you had to do is look at their raggedy hands and feet. They were all groupies in the club and car hops outside. But I had a ball that night.

At home after the club, I was laying in bed again, chillin', reminiscing, thinking about how everything was going. The world would play through my head so I could see where my life was. 1994. A nigga had paper, his business, Craig got his record deal through Paul Stewart, PMP Productions. I dumped him the Iroq. I was layin' in the bed and my world

Chapter 6

was spinnin' faster, to a point where it wasn't out of control yet, but it was getting there. With that thought, my mind went spinning, and a mothafucka fell asleep.

The next day was business as usual. I had a couple of cats coming from Arkansas for 10 keys, and these other cats from Louisiana who wanted work too. In this game, you had to sit, wait, and play the game. Mothafuckas would try to see if they could find it at a cheaper price and give me the run around and shit. By the end of the day I sold about 15- 20 keys and made $5,000.00 a pop.

In the hood I grew up in there were a few cats around here makin' paper. We were the few mothafuckas in Compton, Los Angeles County, who really got work. There were niggas down the street makin' paper, around the corner making paper, so we would have some nice dice games goin' 2 or 3 days a week.

On this particular day at the spot out in Compton, mothafuckas came through. There were mothafuckas from Santana, Hoover, Grape Street, hanging in hood on this day. We were in the front of the house shooting dice. It started getting crowded with at least $50,000.00 out in this game. We took it into the garage to avoid a drive-bys on us. My spot was right on the corner. We headed to the garage and closed the door. There were 3 different games going. Since I was raised around shooting dice and I've been back and forth to Vegas, I understood the game.

I Gotta Get Out the Hood

This is how I get down on dice. A mothafucka started with $5.00 -$10.00 a roll. With everybody dropping 5s and 10s, there was gang of change on the ground. Every time somebody dropped a gang of 5s or 10s I picked it up and drop a 20. What I was trying to do was turn this from a little game to a big game. I wanted to filter out anyone who didn't have real money. I took it to a $50.00 dice game. One nigga and I were going at it.

" I'll shoot you for $200.00."

"Shoot then, nigga! You ain't said shit!"

We had 3 or 4 niggas in a game with $5,000.00 to $10,000 in their pocket.

I caught a nine. I bet you. I back door this nine on one roll, bam, I drop $200.00. Jump him! I hit that mothafucka back door nine on his ass. So I just came up on him and he was getting kinda salty. Now, I caught a ten. "Nigga, what you wanna do with a ten?" Most niggas are scared of a ten.

"Nigga bet. What u tryna do?!!"

Bam, I drop $500.00, he dropped $500.00 and this other nigga said, "Nigga, I bet you $500.00 you don't hit it." So I dropped $500.00 on him. Niggas want some of that too. So I had $1,500.00 in bets, $200.00 on the roll. I had $1,700.00 down there all together. Two other cats came in and bet $500.00. I wasn't giving a fuck. This wasn't nothing but money. I had $2,500.00 on this roll. "Nigga who else in here want some of this shit?!!" I was tryin' to get everybody to

Chapter 6

that game right there. Two more cats came, and I had $3,700.00 on that roll. "Oh, shit. Mothafucka threw a four!" Bam! Mothafucka threw a five. Bam!

"Shit, here come, 55." That was my mothafuckin' foot ball number. I jumped 55. I didn't throw it. I threw a nine. "Oh, shit. They getting' bigger. Oop jump eleven, oh shit!" A nigga lost his mothafuckin' self. I jumped ten but I didn't throw that mothafuckin' ten. "Here go twelve!" I didn't even low ride but I threw this mothafuckin' 64 on 'em. I had everybody around now, 'cause I took the 5's, 10's and 20's out the game. I wasn't scared of no numbers on the dice, 'cause I DID this shit. I was talking shit. I probably hit for $10,000.00 to $11,000.00. One of my other homeboys caught the dice 'cause I fell off.

I had niggas scared of me now. They didn't want to fuck with me. He got on the dice we had $200.00 on the floor. I was talking shit to him, "Bet yo ten nigga. You scared? Don't turn into no hoe ass nigga now. You scared?"

"Kevin, you talking too much shit now."

"Nigga, fuck you. When you roll the dice I'm gonna stomp my feet and you gonna roll a bitch ass seven."

He threw the dice I stomped my feet, "I jump seven". He was salty as a mothafucka. "Kevin, I'm telling you, you talking a little too much shit, homie!" He kinda reached for his gun. I got a 357 magnum on me, I pulled it out. "Nigga, you in my mothafuckin' garage. I tell you what, I'll shoot yo ass right here, right now, and ain't shit gon' happen. I'll call the police and say yo mothafuckin' ass broke in here nigga. I don't give a fuck, you ain't about to try to come at me like this. Matter of fact, fuck that, everybody get up outta here. Dice game over." Everybody, got mad, "Dawg, why you trippin'?"

"You always be over here with this bully shit, homie. Leave nigga."

"Y'all ain't gotta tell him shit, I'm done, game over. Nigga this is my house, game over, shit ain't about to go down like this. Fuck it then, everybody put the guns up and we can do this but it about to go down like that out here." So we continue to shoot a little dice. Hours go by, we might be back there like 7, 8 hours. I think we broke it up at like three in the morning. So everybody leaves and its Hennessey bottles in there, 40 ounces, mothafucka got Cisco in there, gin bottles. So I decided to clean up my garage. I go over to where the guns are and somebody done stole my mothafuckin' 357, I'm like ain't this a bitch! One of these scandalous ass mothafuckas done stole my gun. So I asked a couple of cats, everybody says naw, naw. So what the fuck, I just lost a nice little piece. But I wasn't trippin, shit. Wasn't registered to me. I got it from this cat I get my guns from.

I just walked on in the house, laid in the bed thinkin', "Man! I can't believe what the fuck just happened tonight. I almost had to shoot a mothafucka and almost got shot. You livin' in the hood. This shit ain't cool, dawg. If homeboy tried to test you like that, it's just a matter of time."

Back in the day, when I first got in the game, when I was moving weed, someone sent this little young cat up into my house. My girl's brother was staying there and he heard some noise upstairs and got scared. He ran outside and told the cats outside, "Man, it's somebody up in the house!" One of my boys called me, "KEVIN somebody up in yo house!" I was at the drive-in with my girl and I said, "What! Somebody in my house?"

"Yeah, Bari just came out and told us. Charles just went up in there to see what's goin on."

I flew home. By the time I got home everybody was outside of my house. "What the fuck happened?" I really hoped Bari was alright, that nothing happened to him. When I pulled up, I hopped out grittin', mad as a mothafucka. Charles walks up saying, "I shot him man, I shot him!"

"You shot him!?"

"Yeah, man. I got scared and I shot him."

"Who did you shoot?"

"Deon was in yo house man. He was hiding in the closet. I just heard something so I shot through the closet."

Deon was a young cat, probably about 15 years. I was mad as a mothafucka.

"Alright, Charles. Good lookin'."

He looked at me like he was expecting something.

I Gotta Get Out the Hood

"Good lookin'?"

"Nigga, didn't nobody tell you to mothafuckin' come over here. What you think, I owe you something? As mad as I am dawg, all I'ma tell you is good lookin'. Now go on, dawg . Get up outta my face."

So I went across the street and I knocked on Deon's door. I liked and respected his parents.

"Joy, is big Deon here?"

"Yeah. What's wrong?"

"You know, Deon broke into my house tonight."

"I know I heard. We ended up having to take him to the hospital."

"Is he here?"

"Naw."

"Where's big Deon?"

He came to the door.

"You know, your son is kinda getting out here. He's hangin' out with these niggas over here and they corrupting him. That was kinda bold for him to go up in my house. But I know it wasn't him. I just wanna know who put him up to it so I can watch my back."

I know he wouldn't do anything like that. I respected him and he respected me. But when you tryna be in the hood and you hanging around mothafuckas that's gang bangin', you think that's the shit 'cause you wanna be down with 'em.

Chapter 6

"You know, Deon. I'ma tell you, man. I'm happy that I wasn't home, because yo son would probably be dead right now. I wouldn't have just shot one bullet through the door. I would have emptied my gun in the door and that would have been it. I really wish you guys would talk to him because that was a close call."

I was outside all night, mad, "If I catch this lil' mothafucka, man, I'm telling you…" I really didn't want to do anything to him, but I was just so mad! I went in the back and I got my rott. If I saw that mothafucka I was just gon' let my dog eat his little ass up. I saw a little cat down the street thinking it was him. I went down there with my dog and I was really fittin' to let my dog eat this mothafucka, but it wasn't him.

Over the next few weeks, he was runnin' and hiding and shit. I caught him one day and he couldn't get away. I calmed down by then, so I said, "What's up Deon, man? All I wanna know is who put you up to it so I'll know how to watch my back? That's all I'm saying, just let me know who put you up to it. I ain't gon' say shit 'cause I know you tryna be from the hood. So just let me know who did it."

He whispered in my ear and put me up on game about who did it. Now these mothafuckas around the corner, they scandalous, it's what they do. They beat up each other, they jump each other, they scandalous. I was thinking about that, and what happened earlier at the dice game. I thought I was making too much money. I needed to get up out this hood. If not, I was gonna end up having to kill somebody or they were going to kill me. I didn't really know what to do 'cause I was fucked up. I had been trying to get out the dope game but I kept getting sucked up more and more. It was at the point where murder was about to start coming in my life and I was not a killer. If you fuck with my family that's a different story, but just on the strength over some money or some bull shit- that ain't really in me. So I fell asleep real uneasy, real leery. Every time I heard something I was up. Every time my dogs barked I was up. This was NOT cool.

The next day I got up to get a paper looking for something to Lease and buy. When I first got out of high school and worked for the pipe line company, and we worked on jobs all over so I was really familiar with a lot of places from Diego to up North, all through Cali. Where did I really want to live? I started looking out in Chino. I found a house with 5 bedroom house, 3 car garage, with 3 baths. That shit sounded cool right there. I could park my cars outside.

I rode out there and looked at the place. It was cool. The owner was a little fat cat that just went through a divorce and he was struggling. He gave me the lease with the option to buy. The lease was $1,400.00, his mortgage was $1,800.00. "You pay $1,400.00 Okay?"

I agreed and he said we'd work something out. I gave him $5,000.00 up front. He wasn't really trippin' on the

Chapter 6

application. I wanted something in writing. So we filled out some bull shit. I was young, still 23 ain't turned 24 yet. I knew what I was out there doing so I wasn't really trying to get nothing in my name anyway. So instead of leasing with the option to buy, I was basically renting this mans house, so he can do me at anytime. I shot him some money and he gave me the bull shit lease agreement. "Okay cool!"

Now I was out there by myself, sitting up in this house.

"This shit is me right here, for real, this shit is ME!"

I was loving this shit. I had all this space. I was really about to be this playa playa mothafucka. I was really fittin' to do this shit. I took it to a whole 'nother level. A mothafucka had been in condos and apartments, but nothing like this. Imagine out in Chino, in fuckin 1994! I was just sittin' out there ready to pimp this mothafucka out. I was excited pretty much for that whole day.

I called a cleaning service to have them come out there but they say they didn't do same day service.

"Well, whatever you charge in order for me to get same day service is fine, I NEED that."

So they got there to clean the place up. The owner had a lot of junk in there. My father owned trucks for his scrap metal company, so I called him, "Hey, Pops. Can I use the truck". He's like sure son. I had been driving trucks for a long time since pops was in the business. I learned how to drive at the age of 14. I was also driving trucks at the

I Gotta Get Out the Hood

pipeline company. So I drove out to Compton to pick up pops' truck, grabbed some of my homeboys and paid them a little change to come help, and headed back out to Chino. So we took all this shit out this fucking garage out the house. We cleaned the mothafucka up. I spent the whole day doing that.

Cats were callin' me. If James wasn't around, wasn't really too much gonna be happenin' today. They were kinda salty 'cause you playin' with somebody money. I called James as if I wasn't even doing nothing today. If anybody called me, I told them to call James. He handled everything that day, and held on to the money. He knew where to put the money if I didn't come back. So I wasn't even thinking about what he was doing. I was just tryna get my place together. I worked all day on that place.

Chapter 7

Do You Know Who That Is?

The next day, Craig was in the studio working on a song, "I'm a Star in the Ghetto". The first song he recorded was "The Caper." The shit was crackin'. Big Jess from Watts Up produced it. We were working with Tone Toven of Tone productions. He produced, "I'm a Star in the Ghetto" and sampled, "Ridin' High".

This is how I was feelin'. I just got a 5 bedroom house with a 3 car garage. Mothafucka rollin' the cleanest whip out there on the streets, had the restaurant crackin', had Yahweh entertainment crackin. I was feelin' my mothafuckin' oats.

Do You Know Who That Is?

We were ridin' down La Cienega towards EMI publishing on Sunset. While driving, this broad pulled up on the side of us and asked, "What's that? That shit is phat!" I'm not really trippin' off her though. Bitches flirt with me all day while I'm in my shit. It was the new Supra. Craig is tappin' me on my mothafuckin' leg, "Do you know who that is?!"

"No, I don't care."

"That's Lyte!"

"Lyte, who?"

"MC Lyte!!"

"...what?"

That was MC Lyte jockin' a mothafucka like this? I caught up to her. She said, "Nothing. Yo shit is phat!"

"Cool, but what's up with you? I'm tryna holla at you."

She laughed and shit.

"I'm serious what's up with you? Where you on your way to?"

"Nowhere. I'm just tryna run a few errands."

"So check this out. Let's exchange numbers and try to hook up."

She hollered out her number and I threw a business card in her window. I kept my business cards now. That's the thing to do when you have a business.

We went on in the studio to record a song. The shit was bangin'. I was really feelin' good. Later on that night I hit her

Chapter 7

up and we talked a little bit. I just busted me a little chick from the industry. That was kinda cool.

I was thinking about finishing my shit. I had to finish my house. There was a place called Italy 2000 on Wilshire. I had been looking at this place for years and they had some fly ass shit. Back in the day my mom used to take us to Beverly Hills all the time to shop. Her favorite places were Neiman Marcus and I Magnum. After we got a little older, she had her money to do what she wanted with it. So every time we passed Italy 2000 on the way to Beverly Hills, I used to look at the place and think, "Man, one day, one day I'm gonna go in there and get me something." I never went in there until that day because I knew I couldn't afford it back then. That's where I intended to furnish my shit. When I walked up in there I lost my mothafuckin' mind, dawg. I LOST my mind. They had a black lacquer bedroom set with acrylic lights on the side, a headboard with lights in it, they had pyramid acrylic lamps. I could just see this shit in my bedroom, so I asked how much it was. He said it was $4,500.00. "OK, I want that. How much are the lamps?" $1,200.00 "OK I want them." I guess he thought I was playing. I was young and a little mothafucka. I looked like a little boy. So we walked around the place and I got the bedroom situated. I bought a Mitsubishi 50" big screen that I just bought for $500.00. It was gonna look real kosher in the mothafuckin' bedroom. Now what did I want to do with the living room? The carpet

Do You Know Who That Is?

was peach, the curtains were peach and gray. I saw a bomb ass picture that was peach and gray with white swirls and acrylic glass. It was the shit! That shit was gonna be bad as a mothafucka on my wall. There was a big ass space on the wall in the living room/dining room area between two windows. I looked around and saw a lamp that looked like some shit off of Superman. That shit was crazy and that's how this lamp looked and it matched the picture to the tee. The lamp was $2,000.00 You can do the math as to how much all this shit costs. He handed me the bill told him I needed a better deal since I was paying in cash. He reduced the price, I gave him half the money and told him if he could deliver by Friday I'd take it. I told him to consider what I gave him the deposit and put on the receipt if the furniture is not delivered by Friday then I get my money back. If he delivered by Friday I would pay the balance in full at that time. Now there was another spot off the 60 that I had been lookin at every time I rode up and down the freeway. The 60 is the highway between LA and Riverside. I had cats in Riverside that I did business with, so I was up and down the 60 a lot. This one spot looked like they had some nice pieces so I decided to go up in there. I had a stair case in my house that had a blank wall. So when I went in, they had a picture in there that I wanted. It was $500.00 I asked them to deliver it on Friday and gave them half the money up front as I did

Chapter 7

with the other place. I went back across town to Hawthorne because I was determined to get my shit furnished Friday.

There were these white couches at Roma 2000 I liked, so I got those. They had a glass table made out of acrylic with peach seats. I had to have them. That was another $5,000.00 with all the chairs. They also had this unit for the side of the wall that I bought. I work out the same deal with them. Then I went over to Bed, Bath and Beyond, and grabbed my bathroom sets, towels, sheets, bed set. I pretty much took care of EVERYTHING in the house. I wasn't really trippin' off of the other bedrooms. My room was upstairs, along with the other three rooms. There was a room downstairs. I turned that into an office. Two of the bedrooms were for my kids; one for my son and one for my daughter. I had a guest room, and everything else was pretty much whatever.

I really wanted to finish my room, the living room, dining room, the den and have some pictures on the wall. I got some bull shit green and black leather furniture for the den. It was bullshit compared to the other rooms. The back of the house was a creamish color, and the green and black set it off. It was cozy back there because it had a fireplace too. I called my homeboys to see if they had more big screen TV's that I could pick up. Everything was furnished, and I was still feeling good, having a nice little day. I asked James to handle the business so I could take care of some things. I didn't want to handle any more work that week. James was good at it now, so I just referred all the calls to him.

I called Lyte to see if I could shoot out to her spot. She said it was cool, that she was just chilling with her home girls. So I got dressed in some white Guess jeans, my ostrich cowboy boots with my belt, my matching Guess jacket and matching shirt. Back then it was cool to tuck your shirt in and show your belt with your matching boots, so I tuck my shit in. Lyte asked if I got high because she wanted me to bring her some weed. I didn't, but I agreed to bring her some. I stopped by one of my homeboy's spot to pick up some shit. When I got out there, I walked in and I saw Lyte, Nefertiti, and this cute little Hispanic broad. She had some cool friends. They looked me up and down, "You right, Lyte. He is cute. Little, but cute." I was all blushing and shit. I gave them the sack and chilled with them for a minute before I rolled out because she had to get back to the studio.

The next day I went back to working on my place tryna get shit together. I holla'd at Lyte again to see what she was doing. I was really tryna get to know her to see what kind of chick she was 'cause the phone conversations were cool. "When can we hook up?" She said she couldn't do nothing that night because she had a show, but she invited me to come to the show. It was near the 605 freeway and the 60 freeway, not too far from my house. I called my brother-in-law, Dave, to come out and help me with some stuff. We put

Chapter 7

dimmer lights around the house, installed chandeliers, changed the outlets, put glass receptacles all throughout the house, light switches, hooking it up so it would be ready for the furniture on Friday. One of my homeboys said he heard I cracked Lyte. "Nigga you ain't cracked no mothafuckin' Lyte."

"Shit basically she hollered at me! She said she was performing tonight so we'll just shoot up there. Meet me at the club and we'll see."

I could tell he thought I was lying. We got up there, I called her and told her I was outside. She told me she was about to go on stage but just go wait around back. I went back there and told security to let her know I was out here. I waited for a while and she didn't come out, so I told him to tell her I was about to roll out. She came out right after that, gave me a hug and talked for a minute until she had to go back in. My homeboy was like, "Nigga you for real huh?!" She wanted to hang with me earlier that day but I was busy and I don't chase pussy like that, business is business and that comes first. Ain't no guarantee I'm gonna be able to hit anyway.

I went back home and finished my shit. I was excited because my shit was coming the next day. The trucks started pulling up and the neighbors wondered what was going on. Imagine furnishing your shit that quick at 23 years old. Wait 'til the mothafuckas come out here. Its about to go DOWN! I

Do You Know Who That Is?

called my home boy Mel and told him he had to come see this mothafucka. He came out. He said, "Nigga, everybody got a nickname, so I'm about to give you one. I'm gonna call you Nino from here on out." That nigga called me Nino 'til the day he died. He had everybody calling me that shit. It was funny to me because I wasn't no mothafuckin' Nino Brown. I'm Kevin.

Chapter 8

Damn, We Met Russell

Simmons

Later on that night we hit Roxbury. I cracked a couple of chicks from San Diego that night, then headed home. When I got home that night I was talking to myself, "Damn, you on another level, homie. You really on another level."

I was tired, so I set the alarm, put on my shit and went to sleep. I hadn't really been fuckin with work, since I let James handle everything, so the next day I went out there to see what was crackin'. I talked to my esès and everything was

Damn, We Met Russell Simmons

kosher. Dawg got off about 40 chickens at $2,000 a pop so I owed him $40,000. I went out there on Saturday and checked on my shit, counted and sorted the money. It was all cool.

Sunday was family day, so my family and I went to the beach then to grab something to eat. Deborah thought it was nice, but I could tell she was kinda salty because she knew what was really about to go down.

Craig had the record deal now, so after "I'm a Star in the Ghetto," we really didn't do anything. We spent that week in the studio trying to get the album together. Russell Simons was really feeling Craig. He picked "The Caper" up for a soundtrack. I had been talking to him on the phone but I hadn't met him in person yet, so we set up a time to meet with him at the Four Seasons hotel in Beverly Hills. He seemed like a cool cat, down to earth. He gave us his cell number and told us to give him a call at any time and let him know how the album was going.

"Damn, we just met Russell Simmons. It's happening, it's really happening! I'm about to be able to stop selling dope."

We were feeling good. Once Craig had a signed deal with an album delivered, he would get his other $30,000 from EMI. The record deal was with PMP Records which, at the time, was part of Def Jam Records. The project had a budget of $150,000.00 and my attorney arranged for our company to receive 13 points. That's good for a new artist.

Chapter 8

Most cats used to get only 4 points. I told Craig, I would take the check and put it in the bank and use $150,000.00 of my own money to do the album.

We recorded a few songs but "The Caper" and "I'm a Star in the Ghetto" were the popular ones.

Over the next few weeks we were grinding. I was half ass at the restaurant. I told my brother-in-law I was busy with the music industry because he thought I was out bull-shittin'. I didn't blame him because he was there during the day and I was supposed to be there at night. I had my little partner Greg and Tyrone, a bunch of young kids, working the restaurant, and they are doing what kids do. We were still doing alright. They didn't know what was really going on, so over the next few weeks things were going cool. I still had to go to the restaurant every night to shut down and count the money. I was in the studio working on the album everyday. One night after we left the studio, I discovered Roscoe's Chicken and Waffles off of Gower in Hollywood. I loved the food, so now every night after we shut the restaurant down or finished up in the studio, we were heading to Roscoe's. It was the hang out spot in Hollywood with some bad ass broads up there.

I got up to call Russell one morning and he asked how Craig was doing. I was feeling good because he remembered us by name. I told him everything was going cool. Around this time Montell Jordan was coming out with his single

Damn, We Met Russell Simmons

"This is How We Do It," and Paul Stewart wanted Craig to rap on it. It was really a whack song if you listen to it. Craig was hardcore so he really didn't wanna rap on it. He didn't want the world to hear him for the first time on some big ole 6'3" doofus nigga, Montell Jordan, shit. I told Craig he was trippin'. He was a new artist and that would give him exposure. He said, "I don't wanna come out like that." I'm thinking to myself, "Craig don't really know the business. He's tight but the world don't know him. This song could blow up, who knows." I couldn't convince him to do it, so fuck it, no big deal.

I went to the studio wearing my diamond beveled watch. Craig, Tutu, Steve, and Brian, were there just having fun, working on some music. Somebody knocked on the door and Jermaine Dupri walked in. I knew about Kris Kross, but I didn't really fuck with the music industry outside of Craig, so I didn't really know who he was. Everybody got quiet. "Who is this nigga?" I thought. I was still talking and he looked at me like, "Who is this?" It became uncomfortable in the room. Steve went out the room with Jermaine, and Brian said, "That was Jermaine right there."

"Who?"

"He owns So So Def."

I was making from $30,000.00 to $90,000.00 a month so I don't care who nobody was. Imagine growing up in Compton and making that kind of money. You don't care

75

who nobody is, you're cocky as fuck, so that's just how I was. Jermaine heard Craig flow before he left and liked him. Steve said, "It might be a good idea if you let Jermaine do your album." Jermaine was tight and he had his sound but he didn't have any rap artists at the time.

Most cats that were coming out were fuckin' with like Dr. Dre. Death Row was cracking. They had Snoop, Kurupt, Daz. They were the shit in the industry. We were pitching ourselves towards Snoop because he was the hottest thing out. We wanted to do the album on a level to where we could fuck with him. Craig was signed to PMP through Def Jam. Paul Stewart had Coolio and he was hot right now too. He had a nice song out that was moving units. Paul's ridin off of Coolio 'cause he was the man right now.

Montell Jordan's song came out and that whack ass shit blew the fuck up! Everybody in the world was singing "This is How We Do It." It was the Mothafuckin' anthem. Craig was trippin, like fuck that nigga. So the bar was set high since we were tryna fuck with Death Row. I knew Craig was harder than Snoop. Snoop was considered whack until Suge blew his ass up. I also now that Craig was hard because Russell Simmons took time out his day to talk to me about Craig. That says a lot in the industry for an artist to have Russell Simmons ear. In his world he's the man, in my world I'm the man.

Damn, We Met Russell Simmons

But I'm tryna get in this world, I'm tryna get in this music industry because this is real money to where I can turn my money over and go legit and I'm straight. In our minds me and Craig is like we don't wanna fuck with Jermaine just to do our whole album, we got Tone and Jess and there tight. So we're planning to fuck with them, Jermaine can do a couple of songs.

Chapter 9

Dr. Dre Bitch Up Over a Game of 8 Ball

There was a cat named Emmanuel signed to EMI that played the piano. He played the boards on one of Dre's albums. Steve hooked us up with Emmanuel to go meet Dr. Dre at his spot in Calabasas. It was a nice little tilt, not very expensive when he moved out there, maybe $400,000.00 - $500,000.00. Shit, my house was $250,000.00. His house wasn't much bigger than mine. "A super producer and this is how his house was?"

Dr. Dre had a studio in his house the he worked out of. He took us into the studio so he could listen to "The Caper" and he couldn't deny the shit was knockin'. Dr. Dre was grooving, feeling the shit, bobbin his head, stomping his feet. He said he liked it, and asked us if we were signed with Paul.

Dr. Dre Bitch Up Over a Game of 8 Ball

We confirmed it and Emmanuel told him we were trying to see if he would do a song with us.

"He's a tight cat, but he may have to work on his flow and delivery a bit. I think I could work with him."

After we talk about the music we walked out of the studio and I noticed Dr. Dre had a real nice pool table in the house.

"You get down?"

"Yeah."

So we started a game. I racked, he broke and missed. I ran the table on him. His son and Michel'le were standing in the room smirking at how beat him.

"You ready to run it back?"

The funny thing about these industry cats is they think you supposed to suck they dick. But I was a street nigga, not an industry nigga. He seriously got salty, acting like a little bitch!

"I don't wanna play no more. I got some work to do."

He pretty much kicked us out, and we didn't hear from Dre again, NEVER. "Ain't this a bitch?" This nigga got mad because I beat him at pool. What kind of bitch shit is that? "Nigga if you lost, you lost. Did you recognize I got skills and you just got a pool table in yo house for decoration and when yo homeboys come over they let you win and shit?" He should have kept his weak ass off the table if he knew he wasn't that good. I'm not going to play some shit and not try to win. That's what real men do. They give it their best. So now in my head I thought. "Fuck Dre".

Some time had gone by and summer was over. It was about August 1994. PMP and Def Jam got into it over artists. I don't know who it was, but Paul had an artist and he ended splitting from Def Jam. PMP kept some of the artists and Def Jam kept some. Craig was tucked in the middle of the shuffle and we still hadn't gotten our check yet. We met with Paul to figure out what was happening. He said Def Jam likes Craig but they don't know if they wanna keep him. I had spent a lot of money on the project and in the studio, so I really needed to know what was going down. I called Russell and he told me I needed to talk to Leor, but I didn't know who he was at the time. I got his number from Russell and called him up and introduced myself. We went to the Def Jam, Los Angeles. Leor was looking at Craig, "I like your music, you're really talented but what is your image gonna be?" We were confused because we didn't really know the industry like that yet. Leor says "At Def Jam we sell images. Look at Run DMC, Method Man, Wu-Tang Clan." When I thought about what he was saying, I was like, "Damn, I don't know what to say." He told us to go back and think about what Craig's image was going to be, come back and meet with him about it. We didn't know what to do. Craig said he's an artist not a pimp, so he wasn't about to put a perm in his hair. "I'm not a gang banger so I'm not about to come like I'm bangin'." So

Dr. Dre Bitch Up Over a Game of 8 Ball

Craig and Big Mike, his younger brother, and I went to a couple of malls. We saw this sports shop at the Cerritos Mall and he saw this North Carolina jersey he was feeling, so he grabbed that, some jeans and some nice kicks. Mike was sittin' back like, "I want some too!" So he got some and some shoes too. We liked the way Craig look came out. We called up Leor and told him we think we got it together. We set up a meeting and went back up to the office. He didn't really like what Craig had on. "Look Leor, we're new to this! What do YOU want Craig's image to be. He has good music and when you have good music it lasts forever." We didn't want to be an artist who, once their image is blemished, they're gone. MC Hammer was a prime example. Once his image played out, he was no good to the industry. Once the pants on backwards went out of style, Kris Kross was gone too. That is not what we were trying to be.

"I've sold millions of records with Run DMC. I've promoted the best concerts with them." Craig was getting emotional around this time. He told him he never bought a Run DMC album, never been to a Run DMC concert. Leor started to get emotional too. So Leor said he would give it some thought and come back to it in a few days.

I was worried the entire weekend about what Leor was contemplating. Later on that night, I hit Fritz and got a few table dances. I cracked this chick who was BADDER than Halle Berry. I had seen her before but I never really looked at

81

her. That night, she had her hair cut just like Halle Berry and that's what made me recognize her ass. I told her I was tired tonight but wanted to exchange numbers to hook up another time. She couldn't give me her number at work, so I wrote mine down and slid it to her.

Family Day, Sunday, rolled around again as usual so Deborah and I had a ball with the kids. Now I was back to buggin', because this man had put me on hold. "I don't like waiting and I don't have to wait." That was my attitude.

On Monday we called Leor and his secretary answers his phone for him, "Leor's busy". We figured now he was playing with us so we went up to EMI, which is not too far from Def Jam. We talked to Steve for a while then we went up to Def Jam. We met Tina Davis from the Bay Area, who was just getting her start up there. She said she didn't know where he was or when he was coming back. It was around 2:00pm so we decide to go eat and invited Tina to come along with us to Benihana's off of La Cienega and Wilshire. She was a real cool chick. She told us about how she got started, and came out here from Oakland. We stayed there for about an hour talking about life and the industry in general.

When we got back, Leor still hadn't called back. We were getting ready to leave and low and behold, it was Leor's mothafuckin' ass getting off the elevator. I said, "Leor what's up. Are you giving us the run around? This is our life you're playing with. We don't know if we're signed with Def Jam or

Dr. Dre Bitch Up Over a Game of 8 Ball

PMP. We don't know WHAT'S goin on. Russell told us to talk you and you ain't telling us shit. We're stuck man!" He said he was in a rush and asked if we could meet later or would that be fucked up?

"Leor, that would be fucked up. You keep telling us what you gonna do but you ain't doing nothing."

The elevator's going up.

" I don't really like you guys attitudes, so we're gonna drop you. Tell Paul we'll give him back his contract for you guys and that's it."

Its cool with me, fuck it. I didn't know who Leor was, he got money, I got money. It wasn't about him and me. I was looking out for my artist's best interests.

"You guys are cocky. Let's see if you have this attitude in ten years."

We went back to Paul and told him Leor was gonna let us out the contract. I called Russell and told him the same and asked if there was anything he could do. He basically told me if that's what Leor said, then that's what it is. I had to ask Paul who Leor was. He just so happens to be Russell Simmons right hand man. We ended up losing the record deal.

Paul was trying to go over to Loud records. But he wasn't giving us any money. We still had to work. We met another tight producer, Bosco, and told him what happened. I had been paying for demos, $500.00 to $1,500.00 a song. We

Chapter 9

probably had about 15-20 songs in. We went back to Steve and asked him to holla at Jermaine again, but he had another project he was working on at the time. So we decided to just keep making music, until another deal came along.

Chapter 10

Take It or Leave It

We told Steve we were going to stick with him. He brought us this far, got us the record deal, so we family. I got home one night and laid up with my thoughts. We just lost this record deal but I still had the restaurant going. I had been fucking up. I hadn't been at the restaurant and fell asleep with that on my mind.

The next day I got up and made a few calls to some of my old co-workers at McDonnell Douglas to tell them about the restaurant and see if they wanted to start placing orders. Every Friday we got about 150-200 orders going out there. I promoted at City Hall so now we had that going. I'm was trying to get the restaurant back going 'cause I fucked up. When you have multiple businesses going you can't lose focus on one for the next. If you cant keep your focus on all of them the best thing to do is let something go before you run them all to the ground.

1995. I had been really handling business. My situation with Deborah was what it was and I had this nice house out in Chino. I felt like I needed to just take some time off to clear my head. I went up to Fritz to get Ray. She wasn't doing anything that night. I asked if she was staying there and she said, "No, not if I can mess with you!" I told her I stay out in Chino and asked if she wanted to come out there with me. She followed me to the house. I got her home and the way I cleared my head was GREAT, 'cause she cleared it for me if you know what I mean. We had a good time, fuckin' like rabbits in the rainy weather. We woke up the next morning and Ray was feeling this little pajama- lingerie set I had in there. I let her take it home.

I got up and holla'd at Paul, "What are you going to do?" He still didn't know, so I told him I'd be out there to meet with him.

"Look Paul either you gonna sign Craig and give us a deal or you going to let him go. We're not about to be stuck to you. Steve is shopping us around and while he's doing that I don't wanna be signed to PMP because that's not a good name to be signed to right now." The buzz ain't cool on PMP since he and Russell were into it. He told me to go talk to his attorney, so I went on and did that. He said, "We gave you guys $10,000.00."

"That ain't shit you want it back?"

I told him I was gonna take the contract over to my attorney so he could draw something up and come back. So my attorney Mike wrote something and sent it to Paul's attorney. They played tag with the shit over the next few weeks. I went back up to PMP and told his attorney, "We are getting out of this contract TODAY."

"You're not getting out of this contract."

I put it to him like this, "I am not from the music industry. I'm out here in these mothafuckin' streets. Either you're gonna let us out this contract or you not going to like what's going to happen."

I told Paul, "You need to talk to your attorney. I'm not talking to him no more. I signed with YOU, Craig signed with YOU, so whatever you need to do or say, I'm not coming back here no more after today. You be up and down the streets in your BMW all the time, these ain't my streets but I know a lot of people around here. Whatever you gotta do to let us out this contract I want out TODAY!" He went and talked to him. Dude came back in there grittin' like we were supposed to be scared or something. 'Nigga what?!'" "Here take this contract." We finally got out the contract, cool. I let Steve know we were out so we could start fresh. I

Chapter 10

don't know who all he was shopping us to, but they were feeling us.

We had a homeboy Matt that worked over at Columbia. We were at a club one night and he holla'd at us. "Craig is tight, man. I wanna sign him." I told him we couldn't do that. He was like, " I WANT CRAIG! Whatever I gotta do to get y'all over at Columbia, its done." I said, "Look Matt, I'm out here selling dope and I'm in the streets, I don't know the music industry like that, but loyalty is all we got, and me and Craig are loyal to Steve. That's who got us our publishing deal, that's who got us with PMP, so we believe in his work. We can't fuck with you, it can't go down." We thought Steve had the same love for us. We basically dissed the fuck out of Matt and hurt his feelings.

By the time all these transitions took place, it was summertime again. We made a song called "Reverend Sho' You Right" and it was tight. Shit was feeling good.

I bought a couple of jet skis, 'cause I planned on enjoying my summer. I ain't got shit to pull the skis on. My homeboy Mel had a 454, so I asked him if I could borrow the truck to take the skis out on the water. He wouldn't let me use it.

"Why not?"

"'Cause, I'm not. Ok?"

"Fuck it then!"

Take It or Leave It

Around this time, niggas were buying trucks, riding around in Suburbans and Dooleys with the hips, and big rims. I like to be different, so I went to a Ford dealer and saw this $53,000.00 van on the show room floor. Whenever I go buy my shit, I always look like a bum. So a little young, bummy looking nigga walked in the dealership. None of the white dudes were fucking with me. One young nerdy looking white boy said, "Hey sir! How you doing? Can I help you?" I told him I wanted the van. He opened it up and let me see it. It was nice with a TV's inside. "Ok. I can pimp this shit out." I told him I wanted it. I didn't put shit in my name yet, but I know I can justify this money through Yahweh entertainment. I had been paying myself $4,000.00 a month out of my own money. I took money from the restaurant and recycled it through Yahweh. I was taking my gambling money from Vegas and dropping it back into the company. I told him I wanted my payments around $500.00 dollars. My credit wasn't good since I fucked it off at a young age, as I mentioned. He went in with his boss and ran some numbers. They didn't take me seriously yet. His boss came out, "Sir in order to get your payments at $400.00 - $500.00 you need to put $10,000.00 -$11,000.00 down. I told him I'd give him $8,000.00 cash and write a check for $7,000.00 that's $15,000.00. "Is that good enough?"

"Yeah that's good enough!"

Chapter 10

I went home and got the money, took it back, wrote the check and drove the van off the showroom floor. I was gonna kill 'em with this one. I went to Compton, picked up my mom and dad, and gave 'em a ride. They loved it. The next day I hit up my homeboy Corn who had a music shop. I dropped the van off to him. I spent about $12,000.00 on the van in sounds. My van was knockin'. It was as if I could feel my guts damn near getting ready to pound out. I got heat.

I pulled up to the skatin rink that Thursday and the van was knockin'. I pulled up the shade and got the mood lights going inside, the TV's behind the seats, the TV up top. A nigga just knockin'! So I pulled up, parked my bitch, and got out. I was up in the rink that night chillin'. I couldn't be faded on my mothafuckin' wheels. I was lookin' at all the pretty bitches in there. "Damn, a mothafucka done had quite a few broads up in here." I was on the side rail watchin' everybody, and this one little broad walked up to me, "Kevin."

"What's up, Q?

"You a mess."

"Why you say that?"

"You a cool dude, fun and shit, but just look Kevin. Look at her, look at her and her and her, she just started pointing at all these girls. Kevin, you've had all of them, and me! And I know you ain't used a rubber with them just like you didn't with me. And I know you ate 'em just like you did me."

Take It or Leave It

I'm trippin' cause she's right and it fucked my head up. But fuck it, what was a nigga gon' do? I'm out here in these streets. "*A nigga out here making paper and having fun.*" All I was doing was bustin' bitches and having fun, countin' money. When you're selling drugs, that's what you do. You meet bitches and you fuckin' em. That's what you do. You're in the game. That's part of the life.

After the rink that night, I hopped in the van, and went over to In-N-Out off of Bellflower Blvd. That's where we hung out every night after the skating rink. I pulled up with the shades up, mood lights on. my shit was knockin', playin' "Ain't No Fun". We were chillin', eating, having a good time. My light bright is up there, lookin' at me. We talked for a little while. I hadn't messed with her in a while, but we were cool. I had a lot of love for her.

The next day, it was back to business as usual. I hadn't really been fuckin' around with the streets too much because I was tryin' to get out the game. I was really tryin' to stop selling dope. I hit up Craig and we fucked around. Even though we hadn't gotten a deal we couldn't just lay it down. We had to stay busy because we had invested too much time and money.

1995. I had a taste of what it was like to quit and flip my money around. We went up to EMI and fucked with Steve for a minute. He said everything was cool, not to worry about anything and asked us what we wanted to do. We basically

Chapter 10

just trusted in Steve now, because we believed in him. He said he was gonna keep shopping us and get us a deal and everything would be cool.

I was in the studio, hollerin' at James to make sure everything was alright over the weekend. I made a few call made sure everything was cool and we headed up to Vegas. That was our thang and we hadn't been in a while. We rolled up to Vegas, gambling and I got hit for like $8,000.00 I was like, "Whoa." But I didn't trip. I had these cats coming in from Chicago, I was bout to tear them a new asshole. James got hit too, so we headed back home. We hopped in the van, knockin' all the way back to Compton

As soon as we got back these cats were blowing me up. I'm pretty sure they had been playing the waiting game. They had been hitting me up all week, hitting up other cats trying to find it cheaper. We were in a bit of a drought right now. They were playing this stupid ass game. They called me to say they were on their way. They didn't show up. They called back four or five hours later, asking if I still had it. Evidently their people were full of shit, 'cause they were still fuckin' with me. Only time niggas like this would fuck with me was when there was a drought and they couldn't find the shit anywhere else. I told James not to trip. "We gone' get these nigga this time." I gave 'em a price of $16,500.00. I was only hittin' em for two thousand off each one. They had played me for a couple of days, and now they were waiting

Take It or Leave It

for us to get back. I called and asked them if they were coming through or not. "If y'all ain't coming through after this time I ain't fuckin' wit y'all no more."

A few days went by. I could still afford to give it to them for $16,500.00 but I wasn't. I decided to charge them $18,500.00 which meant I was gonna clear $4,000.00 off each. I told them to take it or leave it. They tried to bargain for $17,500.00. I told them, "Either you want it, or you don't." They wanted to be bad ass niggas like they didn't want it. No big deal!! I had another nigga waiting to come get 20 so I was cool.

They packed their shit up, got their money back and headed for the door. They said, "Man, you serious huh?"

"Look, dude. I'm gonna tell you right now. If you walk out this door I'm not fuckin with y'all no more. It's your choice. Ya'll been playing with me all week. You said you was gonna be ready when I came back from Vegas, I done came back and ya'll still playing. I held this shit and I'm not holding no more work. Either you take it now or you not getting it."

They turned around, "We gotta take it."

So they came back in, got this shit, we counted the money, and they left. It turned out to be a bad and good weekend for me because I lost and made money. I felt kinda crazy 'cause I was slowly getting out the game. I was kinda

Chapter 10

back into a working mans mode, coming back to reality a little bit, about my lifestyle and the kind of life I lead.

Chapter 11

I know It Was Some Fucked-Up Shit to Say

It got late and I went up to the restaurant to close up then went on our regular round up to Roscoe's. On this particular night there were 4 or 5 bad broads in there. There was one in particular that I was making eye contact with. I told my partner I was gonna get her. I went to holla at her, we exchanged names, had a little conversation and I left her my card, letting her know I hoped to hear from her. "Watch how I do this," I told my homeboy Ty, "She's gonna call me tonight."

"Nigga, she ain't calling you…watch."

Chapter 11

I knew the manager, John, real well at Roscoe's because we frequented the place so much. "John, I wanna take care of that whole table's tab." I took care of the tab and bounced. An hour later I got a call.

"This is the girl you met tonight."

"I may have met a lot of girls tonight."

"You know who this is. Stop playing."

"You right. What's up?"

"You paid for the whole table?"

"Yeah, I wanted to take you to dinner tonight but I knew I couldn't since I just met you, and that was gonna be my only way to treat you to dinner."

We talked for another 30-45 minutes, and I had to get off the phone to get some sleep. I hadn't seen my kids in about 3 or 4 days, so I got up the next day and went over to Deborah's house to play with the kids, have fun, and chill with her. I ended up spending the whole day with them.

The next day I got up and went home, grabbed some clothes, and went up to EMI studio to oversee the recording of a song or two. I wasn't in the streets too tough because I wasn't trying to be out here. I really hoped to be off the streets by now, but unfortunately, that's how it went. I wasn't in the studio as much, so I was more or less in these streets. March rolled around and I got a call from this chick I met out in Vegas when I had my supra, asking me if I wanted to go to Magic Mountain with her and her buddies. I told her I'd go,

I Know It Was Some Fucked Up Shit to Say

and told James I'd be gone for the day so he could handle shit. She lived out in Hollywood, little industry, groupie bitch.

I went over there in the Iroq. When I arrived, she look around and said, "Why you come in that car?" I said, "You don't know how many cars I got." Her partners' dudes were all driving Acura's and Infiniti's.

We got to Magic Mountain she started acting funny style, and I let that shit go for about an hour.

"Look if you gonna be acting like this I can just bounce!"

"Whatever!"

So I left her ass up there with her friends. A couple of days went by and she called me.

"How you doing?"

"That was kinda foul how you did a nigga. You that much into cars that you couldn't have fun 'cause you wanted to impress yo bitch ass friends?"

I saw what type of bitch she is. She was real pretty. The bitch is gorgeous

"I apologize. What you doing tonight? You wanna go eat?"

In my mind I wasn't trippin. I was gonna get this bitch. I was gonna do her. I picked her up and took her to Tony Roma's at Citywalk. We had a good time. We kicked it for a day or two.

A few weeks later, I was up in Steve's office at E.M.I and got a call.

Chapter 11

"K. What you doing? I need a refrigerator."

I don't know what type of trick this bitch thinks I am. I played the shit on the speaker for Steve and some homies. I called her back and said, "Look, this is how we gonna do this. I see what type of broad you are and evidently you think I'm some kind of trick. You want what's in my pocket and I want what's in your drawls. I'm gonna get what's in your drawls before you get a dime out of me. So we gonna play?"

"You crazy!"

"Nah, its how you coming at me and I don't like this shit."

We had gone out a few nights, hung out, kicked it, and shit didn't really go anywhere. I fade her off and stopped fucking with her for a few days.

The weekend came around and a nigga went to Vegas. They had a strip club out there called Cheetas and when I tell you, "Whooo shit!" I went up in there and the first thing I saw was this mothafuckin' light skinned Asian and black bitch bent over, knee high black patent leather boots, black g-string, on her pretty brown skin, with long wavy hair. "Ooh shit, I got to get her tonight," is what I told myself. I told the waitress "Here go $20.00. Go up on stage and tell ole girl I wanna holla at her." She did. Ole girl didn't say anything. A few dances go by, and I asked the waitress, "What you tell her?"

"I told her what you said."

I Know It Was Some Fucked Up Shit to Say

"Here go $50.00 more go tell her I'm trying to holla at her."

She went over and whispered in her ear. Ole girl looked over at me and smiled. I was sitting in a booth chillin' cause I didn't want to fuck with nobody. I was getting her tonight.. She came down off the stage and said, "You really wanna holler. You gave her $70.00 to talk to me?"

" I'm tryna take you up outta here tonight. If you don't meet yo quota just come back and holla at me. I'm gonna sit all night and I'm not gonna fuck with nobody but you."

About an hour went by and I was still chilling. She said, "You serious huh?"

"I'm dead serious."

"Look, we got a private room in the back. It's $100.00. We can go back there."

We went back there, and I told her I didn't want a dance. I didn't want anything but to take her up outta there. How much is it gonna cost? She said, "$400.00"

"That's it? Let's go."

"You're dead serious huh?"

"Call the Mirage, give em my name. I'm in a suite. I gamble there all the time."

She went to tell her home girl. Her home girl came back asking, "You wanna take my friend out?"

Chapter 11

"Yeah I wanna take your friend up outta here. Here's my name, my ID, you can call the Mirage and tell em my name and they'll give you all the information."

She went and did her investigation, came back, "Girl he serious." I broke her off the $400.00 and gave it to her friend. Outside I got the Supra valet in the front with the top off and that mothafucka was screamin'. Nobody knew what it was yet, but them 18 inch Antera on that mothafucka looked lovely. Fade any Porsche, Acura, or Viper. It was fading anything on the streets. She said, "What is that? That's nice!" We hopped in the car cruising, top out, her hair was blowing. As we drove down the strip, I was just looking at her thinking how gorgeous she was. There were a gang of people in the Mirage when we got there and they were on this bitch. Lookin' at her and lookin' at me, I walked through this mothafucka like a super star. I had had some bad bitches, but she was up there, probably in the top 5 I ever cracked. We went up to the room. Mothafucka don't waste no time. I ran some bath water, and filled up the tub. We took our clothes off and got in this big ass Jacuzzi tub in the middle of the suite, chilling. You know water makes you lighter so I lift her up out the water and go down there and I'm eatin' this beautiful mothafucka like, "Man." She got out the water and got on the bed, "I'm 'bout to go up in this!!" When I slid up in her she start working her legs like she was riding a bike and I'm like, "Whooo shit." Not that I never had it done, but how she was doing it is real swell, working a nigga. I get ready to cum. Where you want me to cum? She said wherever, I said come here I want you to take it. I put it in her mouth and she slurped it all up and swallowed all of it. I'm like whooo shit, man, when I tell you she swallowed that shit!!! I just paid $400.00 so my shit is not about to go soft, I'm still hard and go back up in there, hittin it from the back know, after that I go back down, eat her some more until she just squirt all over the bed, I turned over she gave me some head. The head that she gave me…was just like wow, as bad as she was the head she gave was even better. She was so bad she made Halle Berry ugly and James Brown beautiful all at the same time. Stacey Dash couldn't fade her, she made her look like a pit-bull fresh out a fight. I'm getting some of the best head I ever had in my life from this bad ass bitch. She get on top of me and ride me like she was a jockey in the Kentucky derby! When I get ready to come she hoped off, and sucked me like she some type of cum freak. I'm like oooooooh shit! So was she worth $400.00 worth it? Nigga YES! it was worth every penny. After we finish freaking and fucking, we fall asleep and I cuddle up with her like she was my girl. How we was doing she could've been my wife this night. The next morning we get dressed, as we going down the elevator everybody is looking at us. It's summer time so

Chapter 11

it's a little windy in Vegas, when we get outside the wind blew her dress up, she bent over and did that little Betty Boop pose. MAN, WOMEN I tell you she didn't have NO panties on, so that made it even more beautiful. Everybody looking at me like you the mothafuckin' man, that nigga got him a bad bitch. I dropped her off, left my number and told her if she's ever in LA to holla at a mothafucka.

I got back at home, sittin' up in my house, lookin' over my life. Shit was kinda cool. I wasn't really trippin' off a lot of shit in my life. I started reminiscing over a lot of the shit that had been through in my house. This house had seen a lot in a short period of time. At one point I had my Deborah living here with me. I thought it was gonna be cool, so I had her move in with me. I gave my daughter a little princess party for her birthday. It was nice, with the family out there. I was just re-playing all these memories in my head about my life and how it was going. I started feeling lonely. The song "A House is Not a Home," by Luther Vandross came on the radio. Having a house didn't seem like enough anymore. It wasn't a home, and I wasn't sure what to do to make it a home, anymore. When I moved Deborah in, everything was the same. The sex hadn't changed, she still didn't really want to cook. I loved her, and wanted to work it out, but I was so far out there, I didn't know how to be faithful. She couldn't accept that, but I knew she loved me.

One day, I was getting ready to bounce. We had been arguing earlier, and she just start crying, "Kevin, why you just can't be right?" My response was the most fucked up shit in the world anyone could say, "I just don't know. Ain't nothing wrong with you, but a nigga like fucking all these broads. So I'm gonna just keep fucking who I wanna fuck and being with who I'm gonna be with." I know it fucked with her. But I was out here, LOST, without God in my life. I had no morals. The streets turned me the fuck out.

I was sitting on the stairs thinking, "You got a girl and kids. She really love's you. Why you can't be right?" I didn't know how to be right. I really didn't. I was turned the fuck out.

I watched my pops cheat on my mom. I watched my brother cheat on his wife. I didn't have a positive role model in my life. I thought that as long as I took care of my girl and treated her right, everything would be okay. I took very good care of her. She wasn't missing anything in her life. Even though I was out in the streets sellin' this dope, I still made time for my family. We went to Disneyland, Universal Studios, Magic Mountain. We hit all the amusement parks throughout the year. I don't miss any holidays. We together every Christmas, every Thanksgiving, every Easter, regardless of what I was doing. She didn't ever see what I did. She only knew because of what I told her. I thought I was

Chapter 11

showing her respect. As a lost man, I didn't understand why she was upset.

My mind was spinning as I reflected over my life. I thought my mama and daddy raised me right. Somewhere up under everything, God was waiting. I sat on the stairs wildin' out, looking around at my 5 bedroom house and all the furniture, money, cars. Tears filled my eyes, and to shake it off I went up to my bedroom and went to sleep.

Chapter 12

Guess Who's in the Club

Next day it was business as usual. I was moving weight. That night, Bar One is crackin'. Bar One opened up, down the street from Roxbury, and they had a whole different breed of broads in there. We were in there chillin'. I saw Jada Pinkett.

I saw her once before at a Jamaican club. She was outside, so I walked out to meet her. I didn't say her name. I asked her name and introduced myself.

"Jada."

"How you doing, Jada my name is Kevin. You got a man?" She looked me up and down with those sexy ass lips, "Yeah, but mmm sometimes I wish I didn't." I knew she was with that little poetic justice, non-actin' good hair mothafucka.

Chapter 12

Back at Bar One. I saw her looking and I waved. She waved back but I wasn't sure if she remembered me. I went over and said what's up to her. She said, "I'm here with my girls tonight so ain't nothing up."

"That's cool. You ain't gotta be so mean." I kinda bounce away. Low and behold, as I turned around, guess who was in the club that night? That old groupie bitch that wanted me to buy her a refrigerator. I knew I'd see her ass again. When I saw her she was with her groupie ass friends. I was geared up, one of the best dressed mothafuckas out there. I spend about $7,000.00-$8,000.00 a month in clothes minimum, so you never saw me in the same thing twice. I was geared the fuck up, and all her friends were jocking, "Girl, who is that, who is that?" I don't know what the fuck she told them. We went outside to talk. I was in the supra this night and it was 'clean. She was trying to floss in front of her friends, run up to the window, "What you doing tonight?"

"Nothing going home, what's up?"

"You want some company?"

"I ain't really tripping. What's up?"

"I'm about to go tell my friends I'm leaving with you."

I didn't know if she was trying to show off for her friends but we were out front in valet and everybody was looking because they knew who I was. Bitches knew me from Roxbury. I was seen, known in this atmosphere now. Nigga had a name for himself. One of my dogs yelled out,

106

Guess Who's in the Club

"Nino, you done cracked that bad bitch." She said, "Nino. Huh?"

"That's what my closest friends call me."

"I kinda like that. Where we going?"

"Out to Chino."

"Ok. I gotta make a stop because my son is at the baby sitters."

In my head I thought, "This bitch is out here like this and she got a kid?" Not that anything is wrong with having a kid, but the way she was carrying herself was more like a single woman with no responsibilities. We went to get her son, put him in the back, and put the top up so the air wouldn't get to him. We pulled up to my house. The van and the Honda were outside and the jet skis were in the garage. "Damn," she said. My shit was fly as a mothafucka; laid out. If I was a broad, I would try to fuck me too. That's how fly my shit was. She was amazed. She said, "Damn, baby. You live better than some stars." In my world, I was a star!

We were in there chillin'. It was about 4 in the morning. She was lookin' for somewhere to lay her son, and tried to put him in my kid's room. I wasn't about to let her use my kids room for her son. "I got a guest bedroom in the back. You can put him in there." We went into my room, and got cleaned up. When she took her clothes off, by no means did she look like she had had a baby. She had chocolate brown skin, a beautiful face, real pretty legs, and silky nice long

Chapter 12

black hair. We were laying down and I was playing with her titties, giving her a massage. I turned and rubbed her all over. I went down licking on her, eatin' her shit and she just went crazy. She came, and I flipped her over, did a 69. She was sucking a mothafucka and I was eating her. I flipped her over again and fucked the shit out this bitch. She was going crazy. I got ready to cum. I pull out and squirt it everywhere, over her ass, her stomach, titties, and all on her face. As soon as I came I looked at her and said, "I told you. I told you I would get in yo drawls before you ever got a penny from me." She just laid there, looking stupid. I didn't give a fuck because she tried to play me. The next day I dropped her and her son off and that's the last I ever saw of this broad.

It was about summer time now and my older sister was looking for a car. I still had the Accord. I told her she could have it and to just pay me when she could. She asked me what I wanted for it, and I told her I wanted to sell it for $11,000.00 but I would give it to her for $9,000.00 She said she couldn't pay me right away but I didn't trip because she was family.

By this time I had been away from the restaurant so long, I just went there to close up. I had fucked my business up by not being there. At this point, the restaurant was costing me money. I told my brother-in-law, "We done fucked this off." I had an idea, since most of the business was in the daytime and I wasn't there at night. I wanted to turn it into a breakfast house. He didn't agree, but decided to go with it. We changed the name to The Breakfast House. The Breakfast House was then open and cracking.

One day I was driving down the 105 freeway, and I saw this cute broad driving in a Saturn. A nigga wasn't passing up anything cute in these streets. I holla'd to her on the freeway. We pulled over. I introduced myself. Her name was Die. We exchanged numbers. We talked over the phone for a few days. She was a real cool girl. One day she called and asked what I was doing. I told her I was at my restaurant. she asked where it was so she could come up there. So she came through and we sat in the back, talking. My sister came back there to speak to me, said hi to Di and kept walking. She stopped about five feet away from the table and came back. She looked at Di and said, "You're that singer girl, huh!" I said, "What singer girl?"

"The girl from Jade."

"Who is Jade? what Jade?! Ohhh, Jade!!!"

I said to Di, 'Look, baby. Check this out. I didn't know who you were and I don't care who you are. We been cool, chopping it up and I ain't really been trippin off you like that. I'm a star in my own world. I don't care who you are."

I fucked with her for about a week, chilling at my house in Compton. One night we just fell asleep on the floor. She seemed like a cool, down to earth girl. I started grooving to her. I was on her now. We went to Disneyland one day and

109

Chapter 12

had a ball. I went over to her house, she came out the bathroom all naked and shit in her robe. I started fucking with her and she said, "No we can't." She was sitting on a nigga playing with my dick and shit. This was our first time in this situation so I wasn't trippin'. I said "You know what? I see you wanna play and I'm not into that. So I'm gonna bounce and you can give me a call when you ready to stop playing and fucking around."

After that night, we went back and forth on the phone. She wanted to hang out but I wasn't fucking with her because she played me. I told her, "If we're not having sex, we ain't going out. I'm not fucking with you." That's just how I was treating her.

A few weeks went by and I got a call. Low and behold it was Di. I told her I was about to go to the skating rink. She wanted to come through before I left. I told her I was leavin' at eight. If she could make it, cool. If not, then oh well. Eight o'clock came and she didn't show up so I bounced. She called again while I was at the Depot.

"Why didn't you wait for me?"

"You said you was coming at eight. You didn't show up. So, I left."

"Where are you?"

"Skate Depot, in Cerritos."

"I'm coming up there."

"Cool, I ain't trippin."

Guess Who's in the Club

I was up there rolling having a ball. She walked up in there and the whole skating rink was whispering, looking and talking. I looked around, wondering what the fuck was going on. I was rolling and rolling and rolling. I passed her on the rail standing with my sister looking at a mothafucka. She was smiling and shit cause I'm doing my thang. I got off the floor outta respect and went to speak. She said, "You can skate your ass off huh?"

"This is my thang, its what I do."

"Are you up here every week?"

"I just wanted to say hi and see how you were doing."

But I still had a half ass attitude because of how she played me. I wasn't trying to fuck with this broad if she wasn't hollering about nothing. After the rink, she asked what I was doing afterwards. I told her I was going to get something to eat then go home. She wanted to come. I told her, "If you're not fucking with me like that, then, no."

"Well, what we gonna get to eat?"

We went to Subway over on Palos Verdes and South Street. We were chilling and talking. Mel said she was cute. I said, "Yeah, dawg. But she's full of shit." About an hour went by and I got ready to go. She wanted to come with me. I told her, "If you not trying to holla at a nigga, or give up nothing, I ain't fucking with you tonight." She said, "Okay, alright." She dropped her car off at the house in Compton and drove out to Chino. We got to the house and we chilled and

Chapter 12

had some fun. I went and took a bath. She started playing again, "What you doing?"

"I'm just chilling, taking a bath."

"Well, I'm not getting in." I started getting mad in the tub. I felt and arm go across my shoulder. Then I feel a little tittie touch me. She got in the tub and she was a gorgeous, beautiful sister. Just gorgeous. When we got in the bed, we just went at it all night. I got ready to cum and she just chasing my dick tryin' to get me to come in her. I pulled away and snatched my shit out. I wasn't about to cum in her. A nigga got kids but they weren't by accident. I dropped her off the next day, shit was kinda cool but it faded off eventually.

Chapter 13

Got To Shake All These Demons

The music business part of my life wasn't working out and it was really hurting me. I was back into the life of a drug dealer. This was the end of summer, 1995. We happened to be at a Rocking Jock softball game chilling with Steve and Jermaine. After the game, Steve was heading up to hotel Nico on La Cienega blvd. The Brat was with them. She liked to call me "The Boot Man" 'cause a nigga kept some type of ostrich or gators, some type of skins on my feet. She wanted me to come by to bring her something. I stopped in the hood and picked up a sack. I saw my little homie Tutu out there. This nigga out there gang banging and shit. I picked him up and took him up to the Nico with me to hang out.

We got up to the Hotel. There were a gang of niggas outside. I pulled up in the Supra and it was pulling eyes as usual when out. I valet the Supra and we walked into the lobby. Everybody was down in the lobby chilling. There were some niggas from New York that had a dice game going. They were shootin' that little 4,5,6 shit. I guess Tutu knew about it. "Kevin, give me some money." So I slid him $100.00 and he got into the dice game. I heard these niggas talking shit, "Aw, nigga. You ain't got no money. Get yo LA ass up outta here." I slid over there, "Nigga, we just bucked yo ass. Get yo LA ass up outta here." I walked over there, "Hold up!" These nigga tryna clown my dawg! "Nigga what y'all shooting?"

"We shootin 4, 5, 6 nigga. What's up?"

"Y'all in LA. Fuck y'all 4, 5, 6 nigga. Shoot 7, 11." I took a $10,000.00 roll of all $100.00 out of my pocket and threw it on the ground. "Nigga shoot this. Whatever the fuck y'all wanna do, shoot 7, 11, nigga. Y'all in LA. Fuck you New York ass niggas."

Puffy heard and said, "Take this shit up to the suite." We all went up there where a gang of niggas had the dice game going. I was in there just fadin' niggas, "Shoot $400.00. Shoot $500.00" Whatever they laid down I was fadin' 'em.

Got To Shake All These Demons

"Y'all tried to clown. Now what?! This what I do. fuck you New York ass niggas this LA." Puffy got mad and came out there, "Man, fuck all you niggas!"

"I tell you what. I'll have a gang of niggas surround this mothafucka, if y'all wanna act a fool. This our town."

Jermaine heard and got everyone over to his suite. We slid up out because it was getting rowdy, and went over to Jermaine's suite. They calmed a nigga down and we talked. "Boy you wild!"

"Fuck that nigga. I don't know that nigga. How they gonna try to clown us like that?" Tutu was fired up but I wasn't trippin'. I had my heat on me.

So we left there. I went home and started thinking *again*. "All you doing out here is fuckin' broads and fuckin' sellin' dope. Are you gonna do any fucking thing with your life? The music thing is not working, fucking restaurant ain't working. What you gonna do with yo life?"

Shit out here was getting high. It was a drought season. Mothafuckin' work is like $23,500.00 a bird so it's only real niggas in the game. These mothafuckin' gang banging ass niggas weren't making no money. There were low riders out here lookin' raggly. Mothafuckas started jackin' niggas, robbin' each other and killing mothafuckas. I was sitting here in these streets. Man I had to get outta this shit! *This ain't the fucking life for me.*

Chapter 13

I let my homeboy move in and shit. I told him I really didn't want any company at my house. He got drunk one night and had a little party. I got home and saw fucking Hennessey bottles, 40 ounce bottles. I smelled weed all in my house. I called him and he was over there passed the fuck out. Normally when I leave, I locked my bedroom door. But this day, I left my shit unlocked. I walked in my room feeling a little leery. My drawers were pulled the fuck out. Mothafuckas done been through my shit. "James, what the fuck happened? Somebody done been in my shit. They stole two watches and a diamond ring. You gonna have to go, homie. You gotta go dawg. You gotta find you a place."

A few weeks later he moved out. I had a homeboy that lived down the street from me. He was in the game too. Now this is when shit started going real bad. The drought done made niggas broke. It was 1996 and niggas in the street that weren't making real money were starting to go broke.

One weekend one of my partners T and I were supposed to go to Vegas but I didn't hear from him so James and I rolled out. When we got back, one of my homeboys came by and told me they got T. They tied him up in his apartment, pulled his fingernails and teeth out, then set him on fire, burning him alive. That shit had me tweakin' cause that was my dawg. I got another call, and they found my other homeboy that lived down the street from me in Chino, dead in his house, laying in his bed, dead, under a fan. I was on 'noid' now. Every time I came home, I backed into my garage. Let me tell you how 'noid' I am. I had an alarm system I can call in to see if my shit had been fucked with, if anyone entered or not. I called every night before I came home. Every time I came home, before I went in the house with my 9mm, I let the dogs in to check every room in my house to make sure it was empty. When I went up stairs to go to sleep in my room, I locked myself with my gun under my pillow. Niggas were getting jacked left and right. A few weeks ago they found this esè in his truck tied up.

"What kind of life have I gotten myself into," was all I was thinking to myself. I was thinking, "This ain't the way it was supposed to be. This ain't for me! I'm about to be out here in these streets, and really have to kill somebody just to survive in this shit. But I'm not a killer." I mean if you fuck with my family that was another story. I could kill for a purpose with a blink of an eye. But over this bullshit? It wasn't worth it. I was deep in the life of what America would call a drug dealer, but I wasn't that. I knew I was out here selling this shit but I wasn't a drug dealer in the sense that I glorified this life. I was fucked because I had really been trying to stop this shit and get out since I got in. I had been trying to start a business to get out from the beginning. Now I was really tweaking the fuck out, because in my mind I had to get out of this game. It was a game where most people lose by going to jail or dying.

117

Chapter 13

In one way or another you lose in a big way. Some people think in life when you lose you still win because of what you gain. Some people think that when you win you still lose because what you lose. That is how it is when you choose to live the life of a drug dealer.

So the question I asked myself was, "What have I gained living the life of a drug dealer? What did I gain by choosing this life when I look at were I am in my life right now?" I fucked up my restaurant, the music industry wasn't working. I thought, with all this money, what the fuck do I have I have no idea what the fuck to do with my life? I had to shake the demons and the scary ass thoughts that were going through my head otherwise risk spinning my life out of control. I was fucking broads with no condoms, but by the grace of God, I hadn't gotten a disease. AIDS was out there and I was gambling with my dick every time I fucked with one of these broads. My older sister had been in my ear about going to church and I didn't want to hear that. But I did want out off these streets. I had enough money saved in the bank and in my safe deposit boxes, so there really was no reason for me to be in the streets anymore.

Chapter 14

The Police Outside

One morning I woke up and there was a foreclosure notice on my house in Chino. The house wasn't in my name since I leased it on a bullshit lease. I got the bank information to find out what was owed on the house. There was a $60,000 balance on the mortgage. I asked the bank if I could bring the money down today to pay it. Since the house was not in my name they could not help me. I had to find the man who owned the house to save it. I called the fat fuck who I leased the house from to discuss what happened. Of course he already knew so he hung up on me, and that was the last time I heard from him. I know how stupid it was, but when you in these streets and you getting money, you tend to do dumb shit because the money is not legal, so it's hard to treat it that way. I decide to move back to Compton until I could buy a house in somebody's name I could trust. My life was in a state of confusion. I had made more money than I knew what to do with. I didn't want to sell dope anymore. I fucked all the bitches I could fuck. I was at an average of at least three different bitches a week. It got to the point were I didn't even want to fuck anymore. I was thinking about being celibate and stop selling dope. My sister was in my ear about God, but I'm not trying to hear it. What the fuck was I going to do?

I had a homeboy that was a new booty to the game. He asked me to help him get rid of some work. I told him I didn't need him. I told him I'd help him get rid of six if he could give them to me for $16,500.00. Just the week before, I was praying to God to take me out of this life, because I didn't know how to quit. A nigga couldn't just walk away from a minimum of at least a $50,000.00 thousand a month and sometimes more. I went to this bike run and came across one of my little partners. He called me later that day and said he needed to get six. I had him meet me in Compton where I did most of my business. That's where I knew it was safe. He didn't want to come out to Compton, so, man, fuck it.

"We don't really want to come to Compton."

"Well, you know what? I got this spot over in Bellflower."

Why I did that shit, I fucking don't know. So fuck it, I told him to go on to Bellflower. He called me two hours late.

The Police Outside

When a mothafucka was late, I stopped fucking with him. But somehow I fucked with him anyway. We were at the house in Bellflower chilling. I ain't never fucked with Tray or his uncle but I knew Tray through my other partner. So we were walking and he was kind of nervous. I told him, "Man, ain't shit fittin' to happen over here." I took my gun out. I had my glock on me this day. I took it out and put it in the cabinet. We were in there just chopping it up. Everything was going kosher, going cool, you know a regular drug deal: we sat waiting for the people to pull up, duffle bag over there, hadn't counted the money since I ain't never fucked with this dude. I didn't know if his people were going to come through or not so I didn't really feel like wasting my time counting the money. I thought I'd just count it later. If it was short I would cover it, no big deal. Finally, after a few hours passed by, I heard the garage open, then James went outside. D went outside, and the next thing you know a mothafuckin' Mexican pulled up. I heard commotion outside, "Nigga give me the work! Nigga give me the work! Nigga give me the work!"

"What the fuck is going on?" I walked to the door. Tray uncle done shoved the mothafuckin' gun in my chest like "Nigga get down!"

"No!" and I slapped the gun, turned around and walked back to the cabinet, to get my mothafuckin' gun, but it wasn't there. I look outside and see this nigga. All I heard was,

121

Chapter 14

"Nigga get down! Get down! Nigga give me the work! Nigga, give me the work! Give me the mothafuckin' work!" I saw this black ass nigga beating a mothafuckin' esè. They were fighting over the drugs. My other homeboy came downstairs. He didn't know what was going on. He had a gun in his hand, and when he heard this shit he aimed out the door. I grabbed his arm, "Shoot em, shoot em, shoot em!" We wrestled over the gun and he wouldn't shoot. Next thing you know, "lak, lak, lak, lak, lak, lak, lak, lak, errrt, lak, lak, lak, lak, lak, lak, lak, errrt, lak, lak, errrt," and my homeboy came up, dumping outside. I leaned to the ground. We went out the front door. These mothafuckas skid out. We hopped in the car, getting ready to chase them. They fucking hitting the corner when the mothafuckin' sheriffs, seven, eight cars deep came, and a helicopter. So, D and I got up in the Mothafuckin' car and went to his house. We were in a van. "Kevin, man what happened?"

"Nigga. them your people! I don't know what the fuck happened nigga!"

I was tweaked the fuck out. I didn't know if James robbed me, if D robbed me, or if my other dawg upstairs done robbed me. I didn't know what the fuck was going on. In my head I was just tweaking the fuck out cause my whole life was spinning out of control. This was the first Mothafuckin' time that a nigga actually had a gun put in his chest.

The Police Outside

When we got to D house, he said, "Man, fuck Carlos. They gone be mad."

"Man, don't worry about that shit. I got Carlos. I've been dealing with Carlos for years. I got Carlos. Don't trip." Nigga, I was mad. Nigga, I just got robbed. Man I was trying to figure this shit out. So Carlos walked in with him and his other esè and Rico. They walked in the Mothafuckin' door. Rico walked in with a gun.

"Rico, put that gun up. If y'all ain't fittin' to do shit with that Mothafuckin' gun put it up. Nigga this the second time I done had a Mothafuckin' gun pulled on me. If you ain't fittin' to use it, Carlos, put it up. Nigga, I know you, and you ain't fittin' to do shit with that mothafucka. Look man, just look. I don't know what the fuck happened. I'ma give y'all fifty thousand dollars tonight until I figure this shit out."

We settled it and they were cool. Now Mothafuckin' D's cousin came over trying to be Mothafuckin' Wild Bill like he was about to do some shit. He came like he was going to save the Mothafuckin' day, and kill somebody with his little thirty eight in hand.

"D what's up cuz. What's up man? This the nigga that got you robbed?" He was pointing at me, crazy mad dogging me.

"Man nah, I don't know what the fuck happened."

"Nigga, shut up."

"Fuck you, nigga."

123

Chapter 14

"Nigga, I'll do you right now, nigga." He put the gun to my Mothafuckin' head like he was fittin' to do me. We by the back door. I grabbed the Mothafuckin' gun while it was in his hand. I said, "Nigga, do me right now nigga, do me right now!" I had the gun and I was hitting it against my head. "Nigga, do me nigga! You ain't fittin' to do nothing nigga. put that Mothafuckin' gun up."

"Nigga I'll…"

D said, "Nigga, he ain't got nothing to do with it."

I said, "Man, fuck this nigga. You ain't got to explain shit to him if he fittin' to do me."

I was crying tears full of anger! I was mad. I was fucked up. I didn't know what the fuck was going on.

"Man, cuz. You lucky."

" I ain't lucky about shit. I done told him I'm going to give him fifty thousand dollars and we going to figure this shit out."

I called Craig and James, they came over, picked me up and we went on our way to the house in Compton.

"Nigga, don't give that nigga shit. Fuck that nigga. Nigga, we can ride on that nigga. Fuck him."

"Man, I'm not even tripping off of that cause all I got to do is make a call to my Asian and I know its going down but I feel bad cause this his first deal." I saw his little daughter crying while all this shit was going on 'cause he lived in a house with his wife and family. He was new to the game like

The Police Outside

I used to be, and I had flashbacks of when I first got in the game and lost work for the first time. At the house in Compton, I got fifty thousand dollars out of the safe. They persisted, "Kevin don't give this to this nigga."

"I'm not even tripping."

I called Tray, "What's up nigga?"

"Man, I don't know. I don't know what happened."

He really didn't know.

Later on, I went back and gave Carlos the fifty thousand dollars, and they were cool with it. It was all part of the game. I called my brother-in-law to tell him what happened. He made some phone calls.

I went home and thought, "This ain't the life for me." I was back in Compton, at the ground roots where I started, around all this shit. I should have known because God had been giving me signs. One day I was laying in bed thinking, "Why is this shit happening?" I went back about three or four months about a situation that happened with the police. There was a drought and birds were going for $23,000.00. I was getting them for $15,000.00 so I thought, "Nigga! I'm fittin' to retire." I was back in the game and really by myself cause I couldn't fuck with James. He was mad at me. He started drinking again, smoking, getting high. I wasn't fucking with him. I was back in this shit by myself, getting ready to make a $100,000.00, nigga, in a day. I already had change stacked. I was going to retire after today.

Chapter 14

My plug just called me and let me know that they just got a thousand birds in, and nobody had work at the time because of the drought. I called about ten of my cats who I knew would come get about fifty birds at a time. Niggas were ready to get back out of town. My homeboy T was the first nigga to come get fifty birds. I gave them to him at $21,500.00. That was $1,500.00 cheaper than what they were going for but I was not giving a fuck. I was getting them at $15,000.00. He didn't give a fuck 'cause he was getting ready to shoot back out to Indiana. The first fifty were gone in minutes of my phone calls. Minutes of him leaving, my other cat hit me.

"I'm ready."

"You gotta wait 'cause the first fifty is gone."

"Damn, nigga you just called me like 20 minutes ago.

"Don't trip. You can get the next fifty."

I'm having my people give me fifty at a time 'cause if something went wrong I didn't want to cover any more than that. I thought it was going down. I was going to dump all this shit today and I was done. I was happy since niggas were lined up, ready. My people just pulled up with fifty more birds, so I hit my other cat, and he was ready. Within ten minutes of my people pulling up, one of my little homies knocked on the door. He said, "KEVIN, man, the police outside."

The Police Outside

"Oh shit!" So I tell my esè the police were outside. We put the work and the money in his car.

"Man, you got to go."

He backed out of my garage, and made a right going down the Mothafuckin' street. I was behind him thinking he was just going to keep going down this residential street. I was going to stop my van in the middle of the street to block them. This nigga made a right on another street. Now the police went around me and got behind him, to follow the work. They pulled this mothafucka over, and caught him on the 91 freeway. These mothafuckin' Compton PD done stole my shit. I know they didn't turn that shit in cause they charged him for aiding and abandonment.

That's what happened a few months earlier. Now I just lost more money 'cause I put my money in his car to buy 20 birds for myself just in case my people ran out. I was thinking, "Man, my whole world is crumbling." I was losing hundreds of thousands at a time!!! I fucked up. All this shit was happening towards the end of '95.

"I quit. I don't want to sell dope no more. I don't want to do this." I still had some change saved and I was ready to quit. I couldn't do it anymore more. I would either have to kill somebody or somebody was going to kill me. It was getting   too   close.

Chapter 15

What the Fuck, Man!

I rode '95 out bringing '96 in as a new man, fresh out the dope game. I was out. I had my life, and I still had money. "I got out before the game got me. Ha Ha! I beat you! Yes!!!"

I remember one night, I met this little cute, light skinned chick. We met up at Roscoe's, and had dinner. I got a call from Pops.

"K don't come home, don't come home."

"Dad, why?"

"The police all up in your house."

I wasn't tripping though. I really didn't care. I knew I didn't have anything up in there. I got to the house, they had my girl's brother outside in handcuffs. My partner Little G

What the Fuck, Man

was in handcuffs. They were sitting in the police car with handcuffs on. I went up to my door, and the police were all over the house.

"Look, whatever y'all find up in here once you pass this line, you ain't got no warrant, so it ain't mine."

They searched every piece of the house. One motherfuckin' cop named T was cursing me out, yelling at me, going off.

"What the fuck did I do to you? I don't even know you. Why the fuck you so mad?"

"Shut the fuck up!"

He slapped the cuffs on me.

"What the fuck, man? Why you so fucking mad at me?"

He was acting like I did something to him personally. They took me all through the house.

"I don't give a fuck what y'all find up in here."

They had the dogs up in there, but I knew they weren't going to find anything, 'cause I got a female pit bull. She was in heat and had been all through the house. So this fucking dumb ass dog, just like dumb ass men, was smelling pussy so he wasn't sniffing for shit. There were no drugs in this house so I really didn't care.

After hours of searching, they found an AK riffle, my 357 magnum, a Ruger 9mm, another 9mm, a 380, another 380, another 9mm. I had a gun in every room. I had a gun in the kitchen, in the closet, in the bathroom. This was how I

129

Chapter 15

was living my life. I was ready for somebody to run up in here and grab me. I had a gun accessible everywhere so that any nigga that came up in my house had to be willing to die.

They took the heat up out my house. I was tweaking the fuck out, again. I had my safe with bills in it and important shit. They found the safe and wanted to know what was in it. "Shit.!" I was in handcuffs thinking, "Oh shit, oh shit!" I was tripping the fuck out. They ordered me to give them the keys. They pulled some keys off of me. They opened it and wasn't nothing in it.

"Ahhhh ha-ha."

They finished searching the house and shit. Remember I sold the Honda to my sister. It just so happened that she just cut me a check and I cashed it. Nine thousand dollars was laying around the house. How could I forget nine thousand dollars in the house? When dealing with hundreds of thousands of dollars, nine thousand dollars wasn't shit. I fucking lost nine thousand dollars in five minutes in a dice game on the street so I wasn't tripping. They found the money, and they took it.

I will never forget Blake, a white Feds. I said, "Y'all gone give me my money back. Y'all ain't got a reason to have me."

Blake said, "You know what. I can get a search warrant or you can let us finish the search."

"Y'all in here now so, fuck it."

What the Fuck, Man

After they found everything, they took the money. On the way out, the cop, T was talking shit. "Yeah, little mothafucka. I got you. Yeah, I got you little mothafucka. I got you!" and he yanked the cuffs up and tightened them Mothafuckas up.

If you've ever been in handcuffs, when somebody yanks your handcuffs up from the middle, from the links in the middle that keep them together, it fucks with your shoulder blades and the cuffs tighten around your wrists, and it hurts.

"Ahhh, man! Can you get him out my face 'cause he drunk and I'm tired of smelling his breath."

"What the fuck I do to you homie?"

"Shut the fuck up."

My Pops was right there. "Dad, you know what. Take a good look at me because you know I don't have no scars on me. I don't know what they gone do to me when I get to the station. They might beat my ass or something. I really don't know what they gone do."

We arrived at the Compton police station, and they put me in a cell. I was sitting in this mothafuckin' cell for the first time outside of the Lynwood police station when I was eighteen. I was pulled over for a pistol. They kept me overnight and let me go. This was the first time I had been in a cell, facing a sentence. They set my bail at two million dollar. I didn't know what was going on. They had me just sitting up in this mothafuckin' jail cell.

Chapter 15

"Yeah, we got you tonight. It's going down. We caught this esè tonight leaving your house. We caught him with seventy five thousand dollars, leaving your house."

I looked over in the next cell and its this esè named Jesse. I looked at Jesse shaking my head. He shook his head back indicating that he didn't say anything. Cool so we don't know each other.

"Yeah, we caught this Mexican leaving your house with seventy five thousand."

"You got pictures? You got proof?

Blake was just observing everything quietly. Ain't saying nothing.

The next morning they took me to Compton court. Compton didn't pick up the case. I didn't know what MDC was at the time. Metropolitan Detention Center. It's a form of county jail for the Feds. They took me down there. I didn't know what that place was. I sat in a big ass hall. They didn't keep me there either. I went back to Compton. I had contacted my attorney, and he assured me that everything was going to be alright. When we got back to Compton, I called my attorney, "Man, I been in here for like three days. You said after three days, they going to have to let me go. After seventy two hours I'm back and they still ain't letting me go." So he called down there. It was a DA reject. I didn't know what a DA reject was. I just knew it was enough to let

What the Fuck, Man

me loose. I took off running straight home. Nigga, my house in Compton wasn't nowhere from Compton PD.

I went up to Compton police after I got out and settled.

"I want my money back. Y'all took my money for no reason."

"You ain't getting shit back."

"Man, I said I got proof of where that money came from. I'm getting my money back."

I went to the bank, got all the information on where I just cashed the check. When I got back to the police station, they sent me to Blake. Blake had to give me my mothafuckin' money back. "Give me my money back. I told you I was getting my money back. He looked back at me, "You owe me. I'ma get you." I snatched my mothafuckin' check out his hand, "Nigga, give me my money," and I walk up outta there.

Early '96. I wasn't really fucking around in these streets. You know a nigga was kind of half ass going to church. I was getting the word a little bit, but I was really fucked up. I was in between now since I didn't want to sell dope no more. I was still half ass selling drugs and going to church trying to change my life. "Man, this ain't really what I want to do." I was selling drugs, going to church, trying to figure out what I wanted to do with my life. I didn't know what direction I was going. I didn't know what I was going to do with my life.

Chapter 16

BOOM, BOOM, BOOM, BOOM, BOOMMM!!!!

Moving into February '96 , everything was going kind of cool. This is the crazy part right here. One night, I went out. I was at the skating rink, having a ball. After the rink, nigga, Deborah had just asked me if I was coming home. I intended to until we got into an argument. I went up to the Hop, pulled this bitch, and fucked with her, killing this shit. I took her back to the house in Compton and all night my mothafuckin' dogs were barking. "What the fuck?" I had this

Boom, Boom, Boom, Boom, Boommm!!!!

little broad I was fucking and hitting so I didn't pay any attention. My dogs were going crazy. I usually don't trip since my dogs bark all the time, but this particular night I didn't know why they were barking crazy but I still wasn't trippin'. After I finished hitting old girl we fell asleep.

I got a knock at the door, "Boom, boom, boom, boom, boom, boom, boom. Boom, boom, boom, boom."

"Who is it?!"

"It's the police."

"Shit. Ain't this a bitch."

I creped down the mothafuckin' stairs, my socks sliding across the mothafuckin' floor. I looked out the window and saw the mothafuckin' police. Nigga, they had at least sixteen to twenty mothafuckas surrounding my house. I opened the door and nigga, they went up in my shit. Nigga, I had drawls and socks on outside. They had baby girl in a mothafuckin' tee shirt with nothing on. My two little partners outside in drawls and socks. They were all through the house.

This time, they took me to a new spot, off of Alameda. As they took me in, I passed twenty, thirty, about forty other mothafuckas that I knew and we all looked at each other, "Damn, damn, damn!" This time they did a mothafuckin' sweep through Compton, Watts, LA, an eighty something people sweep. They got over forty niggas that morning and we were all sitting in there tweaking the fuck out, looking at each other.

135

Chapter 16

"What the fuck is going on out here?"

I sat in there like, "Oh my God." The police came, asking me questions and shit, "You know him? You know him?"

"Naw I don't know nobody. I don't know shit. Nigga, y'all got me up in here. Didn't you see the mothafuckin' movie Beretta? If you can't do the time, don't do the mothafuckin' crime, nigga. Y'all ain't got to ask me shit. Y'all got me."

"Oh, you a little bad ass, huh?"

"Sshhh whatever."

They put the handcuffs on me, nigga. I was sitting in the back of this police car tweaking the fuck out, playing my life over thinking, "How the fuck? How did I get here?" This time when I got to the MDC, I still didn't know what it was. This was the real mothafuckin' deal. They took me in downstairs, and booked me. The Feds were cold, nigga. It was nothing like Compton PD.

When I got to Compton PD, I went to fucking Compton, nigga my first day up in there I remember being arrested in there, now this a holding tank, a little cell man. My first night in there, this big old nigga came in there with a bandage wrapped around his head and shit, looking at me gritting. He had blood on the side of his bandage. I was hopin' this mothafucka wasn't going to fuck with me. He was a big ass nigga, so I imagined the best thing I could do was grab this

136

Boom, Boom, Boom, Boom, Boommm!!!!
big old mothafucka and just start wailing off at his mothafuckin' head where that bandage was, if he fucked with me. That's how Compton was.

But at MDC, it was a whole different story. There were a gang of niggas in there. We were like fucking roaches up in this mothafucka. This is how they did us up in there. When we first came in, they took off our clothes. We had to, strip ass hole naked. Once we stripped ass hole naked, they give us these type of scrubs, with some raggedy ass drawls that we had to put on, fucked up socks with some fucking raggedy ass jelly beans. I put this shit on, and then got processed. Imagine about 300 mothafuckas being processed this way, one by one. That's how it was done.

After being processed, I was handcuffed and put in a holding tank along with the other inmates. We went through this all day, from six in the morning. So by the time we got to court, they had us looking like fucking crooks. The system is cold. They had us looking like savages. We had raggedy ass clothes on in this fucking room, with attorneys all up in there passing us cards. "I'm attorney such and such." I already had my paid attorney so I wasn't really tripping.

My attorney came with the news. They charged me with **CONSPIRACY WITH INTENT TO DISTRIBUTE SIX KILOS OF POWDER COCAINE.**

"What the fuck? I ain't got caught with shit, I don't even know what a conspiracy is."

137

Chapter 16

Everybody was sitting in the courtroom being charged with different things. One dude was being charged with robbery, one dude with selling crack, one dude charged with selling ten keys, another dude was charged with conspiracy for forty keys. Imagine about thirty cats at a time in a courtroom. This shit was wild to me. We requested bail. The court granted it but my house had to be put up. The bail was set at $110,000.

They finished processing me, and shot me upstairs. The Metropolitan Detention Center was nine stories. They took me to the top. I was nervous after hearing stories about niggas scrapping, sticking and all that. I was watching everything. I was on it. I was watching, and looking, but noticed it wasn't as bad as I'd heard, so I eased up but stayed cautious, with my back against the wall.

I saw a few cats that I knew. We were in there chopping it up. Mothafuckas were in there thinking this was the thing to do. I was sitting in there, my first time in jail, you know what I'm saying.

I was able to make a call. I called my girl and she was gritting on me. "When I called over there, after you got arrested, this bitch answered the phone. Who was that?"

"Quit trippin'. I don't know who the fuck she was. Who she say she was?"

"She say she was over there for Greg."

Boom, Boom, Boom, Boom, Boommm!!!!

"Look, man. These mothafucka's telling me I'm facing ten mothafuckin' years. I ain't got time for this shit. I was just calling you to talk to you. Now, if you want to talk, talk. I ain't got time to hear all this shit."

So we talked and as we talked, I started missing her mothafuckin' ass, my kids, and my family. This is my first time in prison. I was playing all this shit in my head, over and over and over again, "Man, I'm in jail, man. I'm being charged for a crime, man. Fuck. God what happened?"

I didn't know what the fuck to do. This was my first night in jail, a real night in real jail. There were two people to a room. The cell was an eight by five vault, with a toilet and a sink. "Damn, man. I'm in jail. I'm really in jail."

That night, I lay up in bed thinking, again, "How the fuck did I get here? How are they charging me with six keys? What is a conspiracy? What is 'intent to distribute'? What are they charging me with? Why ten years in jail? I'm twenty five. What the fuck? What am I gong to do?" I was scared that I was facing ten years for something I didn't even understand. I prayed, "Father, Lord please. You know, don't let this... don't let this be!"

I started thinking back to my girl's brother. He was fucking with this little broad and she had read my palm. She had told me about a bad accident that had happened. The only thing I could think of was the first time I got arrested. Nothing happened, but she said the second time was going to be real bad, and she didn't know the outcome. I thought, this must be it, and the outcome is ten years in prison. Could this be the second accident that she couldn't see clearly?

I thought about my son. He was five, and my daughter was four. In ten years my son would be fifteen, and my daughter would be fourteen. "Oh my God. I'm twenty five. I'll be twenty six this year, and in ten years, I'll be thirty six." I was going crazy in this mothafucka. I didn't want to eat; I was playing this shit in my head over and over, all night long. A nigga didn't sleep.

They said we could get one phone call in the morning, so when they cracked the doors open, I rushed to get in line so I could use the phone. I called my momma and daddy, I called Deborah. She was the only person I really wanted to talk to. I realized we had already been going through it for all these years and I had been a good mothafucka- an unfaithfully good mothafucka. I didn't know any better.

I really missed her and shit. I was going crazy wanting to hear her voice, the kids' voices, and my family's voice. I was in there going crazy, man.

The second day, I called my momma. "Momma, y'all said y'all was going to get me out."

"Son, we're working on it."

When I told mothafuckas I'd be going home, they just responded, "Nigga, you ain't going nowhere."

Boom, Boom, Boom, Boom, Boommm!!!!

All week I was telling niggas, "I'm bailing out of here." The bail was in and we were just waiting for everything to be processed. Five, six days went by. These were the longest six days of my entire life. I was in jail for six days and I couldn't imagine having to do ten years of this shit. "Lord, please Lord. How I'm gone do this?"

I waited for them to call my name to tell me to get my shit. May 22, "K get your shit."

" I'm bailing out!" That's what I was telling myself. They saw I wasn't lying about posting bail. "They didn't have shit on me. I'm out of here! I ain't never coming back here again."

Once I bailed out, and they let me loose, I ran as far away from prison as possible. I called my sister on her phone, "I'm at this phone booth over here. I'm not trying to stay around this fucking prison."

As any nigga or woman that's been in jail could explain, when they crack them doors, you feel like you're in a nightmare, waiting for the fucking prison to grab your arms and yank your ass back in there. It's like a fucking horror movie. You take off running to get as far away from the fucking prison as possible. Then you look back and all you see is a big ass building ready to transform. I felt like I walked out of a fucking plantation, or a pig pen. That's how they treat you up in that fucking place. All I wanted to do was get as far away from prison as I possibly could.

Chapter 16

When Deborah arrived to pick me up I was happy, man, so happy. I sat in the back of the car, "Whoo man. Y'all just don't know. Shit, man. Thank you! I'm so happy! What took y'all so long?" They just laughed at me and shit.

My sister pulled out the Press Telegram. "Kevin, look at this shit."

"What's this?"

"Man, they got you all up in the paper. They got you as ringleader of fucking gangs, car theft. Man, they got you just all tore up."

"Man, ain't none of this shit. I ain't never gangbanged a day in my life. I ain't fucking stole a car. How the fuck they got me as a ringleader?" We kind of laughed it off.

On the way home they kept laughing at me. "Man, what the fuck y'all laughing at?"

"Shit, 'cause look at you. You look all scrungy and shit."

I hadn't had a haircut in a week. A nigga usually got my hair cut twice a week, so I was looking real dirty and scrungy and shit, like a little wet puppy. I could not wait to go get a fresh cut.

We got back to my house, chopped it up for a while, then Deborah went home. I told her I'd be through there later. My homeboys came through to check me out and find out what was going on. Craig came through, "Nigga, you alright?"

"Yeah."

Boom, Boom, Boom, Boom, Boommm!!!!

So we in there chopping it up and Craig was laughing too.

"What's so funny?"

"Nigga, you crazy, nigga. Your brother Nate, that nigga's a fool."

"What?"

"Man, you see what happened when you was in court?"

While I was in court trying to get bail, they mentioned that I had eighteen keys, and how they caught someone leaving my house.

During the raid, they had run up in my momma's house and found a fucking bird up in there too. When I got to my momma's house, they wouldn't let me in. "Sir, you can't come in here."

"This is my momma house what the fuck y'all talking about I can't come here."

"Sir, we found something in this house and we don't know whose it is. So you can't come in."

"What the fuck's going on. What?"

My homeboy down the street was a cop now, and he was all up in the house. My sister and I went over there, "You talked to Nate? Velle? What the fuck's going on?"

No one was answering.

My brother packed his bags and was on his way to Texas with his girl. My older brother said he was out in Hollywood and couldn't come through. Nate done put some work in my momma's house and ain't said shit.

So while I was in court trying to get bail, they brought that shit up, "Yeah we found a kilo of cocaine at your mother's house, you know. We know you've been living out in Hacienda Heights with your wife."

"Hold up, this ain't even me. Before y'all start accusing me of some shit get your people right. I don't live in no Hacienda Heights."

So the judge looked at the paperwork and said, "No, he doesn't live in Hacienda Heights."

"If you talking about that bird that y'all found in my momma house, look at the paperwork. I was standing right there on the front porch. So if it was me y'all would have arrested me then. I ain't got shit to do with none of this. Y'all accusing the *wrong mothafucka*." I actually said, "*Y'all accusing the wrong person, your honor. You need to look at this case and talk to the prosecutor before they start accusing somebody. Make sure they got the right people."

My brother, at the mention of that kilo, said to Craig, "Craig, that wasn't Kevin dope that was mines," then jumped up and bounced, running out of the courtroom.

"If y'all would have seen how fast he ran out that mothafuckin' courtroom, like flash Gordon around here, phewww, phewww, phewww. He was gone; nigga that shit was funny as a mothafucka."

Boom, Boom, Boom, Boom, Boommm!!!!

We chopped that shit up, spitting it up.

My next stop was Sam's barber shop next door to the restaurant. I got a nice little fresh cut, then took a nice little bath. I could not wait to take a bath.

In prison, all I got to do was take showers. I kept my shower shoes on cause mothafuckas up in the shower were jacking off. You could catch all kind of shit up in them showers. I didn't touch the walls. Niggas got boogers and shit all over the walls. Jail is nasty.

I took a bath, sat in the tub, and soaked. Later on that day I got up, went to Deborah's house, saw my kids. I was happy to see them, play with them. I spent the night over there. It had been a week so you know a mothafucka had to get him a little, handle his business and shit you know. That's how that day went.

The next day it was kind of crazy. I met with my attorney. He wanted to discuss his fees. He wanted $50,000.00 to take the case. Well, shit, when I bailed out I gave him $10,000.00 and he kept $5,000.00. How much was he going to take?

"Well, I want fifty."

"Fifty is a lot, and you haven't done nothing. I will just pay you on the back end."

"Okay, cool."

He took the case. We talked about what was going on.

"What they got me on, David?"

Chapter 16

"I don't know. I'm waiting for the tapes. They're saying you were getting ready to sell six kilos of cocaine to someone."

"Where's the evidence? Where's their proof?"

"They haven't turned over the property. They have to file their evidence. Once they do, they have to turn it over to me. We just have to wait and see what happens."

Chapter 17

A Drug Dealer Caught Up With a Case

I had been out there in the streets selling dope with a motto, "Do it until you get caught." Stupid motto but it worked for me.

I was finally caught. I didn't know what the fuck I was gonna do. I played the rest of the week kind of smooth, layin' up with a lot of thoughts, 'cause I was caught now. I was no longer a free drug dealer. I was a drug dealer caught up with a case. When you're out there doing crimes, illegal shit, it's

147

not a crime until you get caught. Then you are prosecuted, and have to face your time.

May going into summer of '1996. I still had everything, the car, the van, a low key Maxima, and that big body Benz with 20inch. There weren't too many niggas rolling on twenties. I was still out there with a little bit of paper. I still had change and shit. Mothafucka wasn't trying to sell dope and niggas weren't trying to fuck with me neither. After getting arrested, I was taboo. You turn into a fucking disease around niggas. Mothafuckas treated me sideways. Niggas I didn't even fuck with were looking at me shady and shit like, "Nigga, how you get out?"

"Nigga I ain't got to explain shit to you."

Other niggas were still up in there.

"Nigga, I don't fuck with you anyway homie."

So these are the conversations I was getting in. I was a plague around this mothafucka. Once you go to jail, you ain't the man any more. You a mothafuckin' plague. Niggas didn't know if you talking, if you telling, if you what. My circle of people that I was fucking with was small, so the good thing was that nobody in my circle went to jail besides me. Mothafuckas weren't looking at that.

"This nigga went to jail. He just got out. We ain't fucking with him."

Right before I went to jail, I was sitting up in church. I had started going to church and I was praying that God

148

would get me out. "This was my way out Lord. This is how You brought me out of this. Did I have to get robbed and go to jail to come up out of this?"

He wasn't answering or talking. I was playing this all in my mind. It had to be. Everything that I normally did I didn't do. I went to James's house. I hadn't been fucking with him. I waited two three hours. I usually never did that. Nigga didn't see the money. I never did that. I let them call all the shots.

"Damn, maybe this was meant to be."

I got this case. I didn't have anything coming in but I still had to find a way to live out here. I hadn't had a job in years. I was on my way to prison. I had two kids. I had my girl, I had all these bills and I was just out there, shit still going. I was still fucking with all these broads out there, nigga still had a few hoes. They felt sorry for me and shit, so I was playing the sorry role. I let them do whatever.

"Baby, you all right? Come on over here tonight."

"Okay cool."

I went by one of my little broad's spot and she had dinner ready for me, lingerie on. She rubbed a nigga's back, gave me a massage. "Oh shit. This shit kind of cool." She gave me some good ass loving.

The next night I went out with one of my other little broads, and shit. We were driving down the freeway, after leaving a movie, and she said, "Baby, you alright?"

149

Chapter 17

"Yeah, I'ma be alright. I ain't really…but, I'ma be alright."

"You sure?"

"Yeah."

"I'ma show you how you gone be alright. I'll make sure you gone be alright."

So she lean over and just started giving a nigga mad dome. Niggas hate on you when you get caught up. Niggas hate. But your broads, nigga, if they love you, they're going to take care of you. I can't say they loved me, because that's a fake word to use when you got a bunch of broads. But I will say they liked me enough to make me think they loved me. They were damn sure in my corner. I was still wilding out. I hadn't found God in my life yet. I didn't know how to cut off my broads and I kept my woman. My woman wasn't really feeling sympathetic for me. She was still just gritting mad, and shit, trying to figure out why that bitch was at my house that morning. She was still on that page. But all my little broads out in the streets were feeling sorry for a nigga.

One night, I went out with another young broad. This is a rundown of what I was going through after I got out of prison over the next few months. I went out with my one little youngster, to the movies. We were sitting up in the movie. "Baby you done had it rough. A lot of shit going on with you."

"Yeah, but everything's cool."

A Drug Dealer Caught Up With a Case

We were in the movie, nigga, and she pulled my shit out and started stroking it. "Man, stop. Kick back." She embarrassed me so she stopped. "You can't take that?"

"Naw, I can't. I really can't take that."

After the movie, while we were in the car she came up out of her clothes. "What you doing?"

"Don't worry about it."

"Kick back. I'm on bail you can't be in my car naked."

She sat up playing with herself. "Oh my God." Not that I hadn't seen this but, I never had a broad do this to me in the car while we were driving. Not in the car. She hopped across from the passenger seat to the driver seat and hopped in my lap trying to ride me.

I was nervous as hell because I was already on bail. If the police pulled us over I was going straight to jail. I wasn't trying to spend another day in jail. Fuck a day. A nigga wasn't trying to spend another *second* in jail. It was the mental battle of being in jail that I wanted to avoid. Six days of mental battle in jail was like an eternity to me. Nasty food, stanky ass niggas doing some crazy shit up in there. In six days I had seen all kinds of nasty shit, from men, up in jail.

"Move girl, move. Get up off of me."

She moved, got in the seat laughing and shit, "Aww you done got scared?" Call it what you want. She was right if I was scared of going back to jail. I didn't know what would happen if the police pulled me over.

151

Chapter 17

All that shit ended that night. While I was out on bail, it wasn't 'business as usual'. I wasn't selling dope so I was basically out in the streets still doing a little music trying to make something crack. When I was out on bail I was spending money as fast as I had made it. My average bills were about $6,000.00 a month. This was the lifestyle I was used to. With no income, I was seeing hundreds fly. These hundred dollar bills were being tossed like fifty dollars worth one dollar bills being thrown at a stripper for fun. Hundred dollar bills were flying through my hands in an unimaginable way.

"Dog, you ain't making no money. You got to kick back."

I was still in this life so there were no drastic changes. Deborah hadn't stopped getting on my nerves, I still liked the strip clubs, I was still at the skating rink. My life didn't stop because I stopped hustlin' It would be like trying to stop a waterfall from flowing. After so many years, it doesn't just stop. Something drastic has to come and stop it.

I had been building a Harley Davidson for the past three years. I used this time to finish my hog, put it together, and show it. That was my thing. Since I didn't have a chance to show it, I got some fun out of it. I told my brother-in-law that I really wanted to rush and finish it. So we took the motor up to Nigel at Patrick Races. He built the motor and the tranny. Mitch at Kelly Paint's had already finished the paint. I got the seat done at this place off of Melrose and La Cienega. All

A Drug Dealer Caught Up With a Case

the pieces were clean. So my brother-in-law finished the bike. He called me and told me to come out there. The bike was a blue, pearl blue with a little fuchsia pink and grey. Kelly painted the shit out my bike. I had pit bulls painted on the tank and handle bars.

I had an 1100 jigseR boarded out to a 1350 that I used to ride. I knew how to ride, but riding this hog was a totally different experience. You can't tuck. I got on the bike the first day and just naturally thought to tuck my legs. When I tucked, the inside of my leg, right by my knee, hit that pipe and burned the shit out of me. I parked the bike, hopped off and, you talking about doing a dance, a nigga was jumping around trying to pull his fucking pants leg up cause that shit was burning like a mothafucka. "Damn!" That was my first accident on a hog. I shook it off.

I got back on the hog, hit a few corners throughout Compton, to show it off. I was trying to make niggas know I was still the mothafucka. That's how I was feeling. I might have gotten cracked, but a nigga was still having paper. So when I pulled it out nigga I hit everywhere. I went up to All Star, anybody who knew All Star in the 90's knew that's where you went. The cars, the bikes, everybody went through that mothafucka. I went up there just to floss.

I acted like I was finna holler at Ruben about some shit. So I pulled up there and niggas were up there gritting like a mother...all I saw on peoples' faces was, "Mother.., ooh,

Chapter 17

damn, man that mothafuckin' bike, that hog, oh my God, it's clean." I saw a couple of my cats.

"What's up dawg?"

"Wassup?"

"Shit, nigga. Wassup, nigga. Y'all don't even fuck with a mothafucka. Nigga, I'm like fucking taboo around here now that I caught my case."

"Awww dawg…"

"Aww dawg what? It ain't no big deal nigga. Do you know anybody in jail? Was I fucking with any of your people? I mean y'all ain't gotta come at me like that. But its cool. I'm not tripping, nigga. I'm still alright. Nigga, I'm still alright."

So I stayed up there for a few minutes to let mothafuckas see the hog. I twisted a few more corners, shot out to LA, twisted some corners. The bike was a mothafucka.

There was a little run at Val Verde park by Castaic lake. We went up there on the bike. I pulled up, fading everything. I had the cleanest bike on the streets at this time. Trust me. In the summer of '96, I had the cleanest bike on the streets. When I pull up to the park, mothafuckas said, "Homie. Nigga. Whoo. Who painted it? Where you get the motor done?" Mind you everybody was powder coating their motors and frames. I was the first nigga that had his motor painted. I didn't powder coat shit. I had it painted. I had my frame painted to match. My bike was clean and if you lived in Compton, you know what bike I'm talking about.

A Drug Dealer Caught Up With a Case

We were at the park, getting ready to leave. Niggas knew it was pretty but questioned if it could run, if it had balls. I hadn't even put any miles on my bike so I couldn't get in it. Anybody that rides bikes knows you can't get in a fresh built motor. They were clowning me and shit, "Pull on off." So when we got to the motorcycle club up in LA where my brother-in-law knew everyone, they continued with, "Yeah, its pretty. That's all it is. But it ain't got no balls." I wasn't tripping. I couldn't really say shit 'cause they whooped my ass. I didn't get in my bike. I played it off, didn't say shit.

They had a pool table at the bike club. I had game on the table so I went up in there and started running through they ass. I started talking shit, "I really couldn't beat y'all ass on my bike, but I'ma get a chance to. Right now, I'm getting in y'all ass in y'all house on this mothafuckin' pool table." They didn't like that, and started getting salty and shit ready to fight. My brother-in-law said, "Let's roll". We cranked up the bikes, I hit the fish tail pipes, and let them roar on they ass and we scoot on out.

He got to the house, I got to mine. You know everything's cool. I went by my Deborah's house, spent a little time with the kids. My typical day now, on bail, was basically waking up, hopping on my hog, wiping it down after I finished riding, and just kind of talking back and forth with my attorney.

Chapter 17

It was around the end of summer, maybe August, September and I called my attorney. He told me they had the evidence in. I went to meet with him, we went through the evidence, and we listened to the tapes. The 'Conspiracy to distribute six kilos of powder cocaine' was from my robbery.

I looked through the evidence given to my attorney. Going back to that day, the gun shots, my missing gun, dealing with new people, the stolen dope, I was putting it all together. The cold part, man, the Feds had all this on tape, and they were waiting for a body. They let the police come in, and didn't try to stop any of it. My homeboy, that I was getting the work, from didn't set me up, but it was his people.

After we lost the work that night, the tapes showed that he get on a phone call to his cousin.

His cousin said, "Yeah, I made a few calls nigga. That was our people."

D said, "Man, can you get it back?"

"Well, no we didn't get it back. But they had one or two of them and we got that. But, you know, don't let that nigga know. Just keep pushing up on him trying to get the money."

D was the one they were after. They were watching him, and one morning he called me on the phone. I was at the house after returning from the dentist getting my teeth fixed. The conversation went, "Man, wassup dawg?"

He said, "Wassup?"

A Drug Dealer Caught Up With a Case

"Shhh nothing man, I just got my tooth pulled and these mothafuckas left a piece of tooth in there. Man, that shit hurt. I fucking got dry socket or something."

"Damn, dawg. Wassup? You going to Frit's tonight?"

"Shit I don't know. If I'm feeling better I might fuck with Frit's. Wassup?"

"If you ain't doing shit, slide through there."

This conversation transpired on my house phone in Compton. The crazy part is, I didn't have anything in my name but that house phone. The wire taps on my cell phone were all transcribed on paper, 'unknown male', 'unknown male', 'unknown male'.

One day I got a letter in the mail from the court saying that they were going to subpoena my phone records from Compton. I thought it was no big deal. Once they received my phone records they ran a voice analysis through the phone from my house in Compton through the cell phone to the 'unknown male'. That's how they came up with a match and got my name. From that match, they found my conversations saying, "Take six to James's house." That's how they charged me with a conspiracy. All because they were watching him.

They caught him with work in Memphis. They were just hitting, hitting, hitting. He thought people were hitting him or robbing him, but it was the police all this time. The Feds were actually on another cat who used D's phone. They

Chapter 17

watched him as he picked up D's phone, then 'boom' they hit D's phone with their tapping equipment. The cat gave the phone back to D and they were on him now. That's how the Feds got on him. And that's how they got on me.

I told my attorney that drugs were never mentioned. "All they had was a dollar amount. I am drug dealer but I didn't sell cocaine. I'm guilty of selling six kilos of marijuana?" My attorney looked at me with a You-think-I'm-stupid? look. "Why are you looking at me like that?" "So you were selling marijuana?"

"Do you see cocaine in here? Yeah I was selling marijuana, that's what it was."

He sat there with an attitude. I looked back at him and said, "Look, dude. If you don't believe me, then you don't have to represent me. I'm paying you. You work for me. Now whether you believe me or not that's what I was selling marijuana."

"Alright, alright, alright."

"You are my attorney. Either you going to work with me or you not."

"Okay. This is how it is then. Fine, we will take that."

He ran that story to the prosecutors. They were salty because I was pleading guilty but to a lesser charge by saying it was marijuana, and not cocaine.

"Oh no, no, no. We're not taking this."

A Drug Dealer Caught Up With a Case

"They said no, Kevin."

"Okay. That's my story. Let's go to trial."

The next few months would be spent preparing for trial.

Later on that week my brother-in-law told me they had another run up at Val Verde park, and if I wanted to roll.

"Okay, yeah. Cool."

So we rolled up there. I had put about 2-3000 miles on my motor since the last time I was up there. The same cats were up there, "He's back with his sissy ass bike. It's pretty but it can't run." I didn't say shit since they done whipped my ass. We had a nice little day.

When we got ready to leave, there was one cat blocking the streets so the bikes could get through. They called me a scary rider. "Call me what you want." Everybody was going out in the streets. I stopped at the stop sign. As I stopped, a '65 Mustang came speeding over the hill. When he saw the cat in the middle of the street, he hit the brakes, "errrrrrrrrrrrrrrt!" The brakes locked up, and he slid out of control, hit the back of another car, and flipped over into a ditch. If I hadn't stopped, he would have hit me dead on. Yeah, call me a scary rider. I'll be that.

After all of this, we hopped on the freeway. The same nigga that wanted to race my bike had his broad on the back of his bike. I pulled up on him and his crew of about twenty cats on they shit. My brother-in-law didn't ride this time. He was in his truck at the front, boning out. Nigel, from Patrick

Chapter 17

Racing, was the shit. When it came to building motorcycles, nobody could fuck with Patrick Racing. I hit the gas and went by all them niggas, barking. My shit was barking like a mothafucka. I got up to the leader, "Let's go." I left his homeboy in the dust, he and his broad. My brother-in-law was in the truck with his homeboy laughing his ass off. They were laughing cause this nigga done talked shit.

When we got to the place, I was flossin', "Yeah, I thought it didn't have balls. It just whipped your bitch ass. Didn't it nigga? Where your shit at? You can't even fade my shit. The mothafucka pretty *and* it got balls. Nigga, I got the cleanest shit on the streets and one of the fastest mothafuckas on the street. Now what?"

They were salty 'cause I was in no motorcycle club. I rolled solo with whatever I did, so I wore all their asses out. I didn't even stay up there this time 'cause I felt the animosity. I just shot through there to let them know, "Nigga what!"

Chapter 18

I Don't Want To Die Lord

I still had a few broads despite dropping most of them. A few years before, I had one real cool, cute little brown shorty, about 5'1", who was always down for a nigga. I had been fucking with her shit for a good four to five years. She was my little partner. I was feeling her at the time, but my situation was what it was.

My little Light Bright from the rink had a dude by now, so she wasn't really fucking with a nigga. She came by to make sure I was alright, though. Her dude kept her in handcuffs and shit so she really couldn't fuck with me. He knew I used to fuck with her so he kept her away from me. It was no big deal.

I was at the rink bugging out, thinking about all the things I had been doing over the years. A nigga was out here on mothafuckin' bail and shit. So I rolled the night out, fucked with a few of my little broads, talked to a few homies.

The next day, I was bugging out and chilling without shit to do. I was on bail, didn't have a job, living off the money that I made, and still living my life. There were a couple cats calling me trying to get down. These were real cats so I still fucked with them. They knew a nigga was straight. But I wasn't trying to get down. I was through selling work, done. I wasn't trying to catch another case.

I still hadn't picked up the bible. I was just listening to my sister. I had stopped by church a few times. One particular Sunday in August I was at the back of the church with my brother-in-law George. I was sitting in the back of the church thinking, "Yada, yada, ya." I wasn't paying attention. I wasn't spiritual. I wasn't in the word. I was out here lost, wilding out.

The pastor said, "You know when God's got his arms around you, can't nobody hurt you. Can't nobody harm you. A man can be almost two feet in front of you with a gun headed straight for you, pointed directly at you, shooting, and not a bullet will touch you. A man could be driving down the street in a car and you could walk across the street. The car will swerve around you and won't hit you."

I sat in the back of the church, "Yeah, right. Whatever, man. This man crazy." This is what I was thinking. I didn't know how God operates. I had no clue of His word, what He's about. I just knew His name was God, The Creator. That's all I knew about God.

I sat in the church as a drug dealer, just getting caught, out here wilding out. I was a non-believer sitting up here making a mockery of God and His word. Making a mockery of this church. I was just laughing my ass off in the back of the church. That was some funny shit to me, a good joke.

The next week about four of my other cats and I were out chilling, hanging out, kicking it late one night on the block. We were talking about life, about what I was doing, about girls, gangbanging, hustling, women, our future, our careers.

"Sometimes man it's so fucked up out here. Sometimes a nigga wish he was dead. Man, I really don't mean that. I rebuke that in the name of Jesus."

"Man, I know. Sometimes I wish I was dead. I be wishing that all the time."

I said, "Man, you really don't believe that. Rebuke that. Take that shit back."

Since we were hanging out down the street, I just rode my mountain bike down. I was still sitting on my bike, with the back tire up against the curb. My homeboy was to the right of me, my other partner was parked the opposite way. We saw some lights from a car pulling up real slow. As it came to a stop, we just heard, "lak, lak, lak, lak, lak, lak,... lak, lak, lak, lak, lak, lak, lak, lak, lak, lak, lak, errrrt." And they took off.

With the first set of shots, I was close enough to feel the fire from the gun. I could hear the bullets, "shooo, shooo, shooo, shooo", passing by my head. Something told me, "You ain't hit! Move fool!" I let the bike fall, and I jumped off and ran behind a tree. I could hear the bullets hit the tree, "Pat, pat, pat, pat!" On the second set of shots, my homeboy was about 15 feet away and said, "I'm hit, I'm hit!" I watched him walk and stumble, walking and stumble. He put his hand up against the tree and he started sliding down the tree praying, "Father, Lord, I'm not ready to die Lord. Not like this Lord, not like this. I don't want to die like this."

He fell to the ground on the curb and leaned over the curb. He had a hole in his neck with blood gushing out like water from a faucet. He patted the ground, "Father, Lord not like this Lord. Not like this. I don't want to die Lord." He kept patting the ground. I looked at him helplessly, in shock. I couldn't think, I was being grabbed.. The neighbor across the street came outside and grabbed him, putting her arm around him and cradled him like a baby. He had a look of fear on his face, eyes wide open while begging God to spare his life. She rocked him, saying, "Just accept Jesus Christ as

I Don't Want To Die Lord

your Lord and savior. Accept Jesus Christ as your Lord and savior!" At that very moment, peace entered his body, and his face was calm. He stopped crying, talking and shaking, with a look of comfort like a baby in his mother's arms. I looked up saying, "Thank you, Lord. Thank you, Lord."

The ambulance arrived along with the police.

The Compton PD knew everything about my case. They done robbed me, arrested me, everything. When the Compton PD pulled up, he said to me, "You sure they weren't shooting at you?"

I didn't even answer him. It was strange to me that he would ask that. This boy was dying and in the ambulance. We weren't sure if he was going to live or die.

Investigating the scene, they noticed that one bullet hit the front of my bike, one bullet hit the pedal, knocked the reflector light off the pedal, one bullet hit the front spoke, one bullet was stuck in the sprocket, broke the chain. So the bullets hit the bike. The officer said, "I don't know how the bullets didn't hit you."

"God. That's how."

I looked at the cop, "You, y'all cold. I mean your hatred for me and your jealousy towards me is so strong that you can't even be concerned about this man." They asked if they were shooting at me when there were four other people out here. He really didn't know who was out there, but that was his only concern, as a peace officer coming to help- how *I* didn't get hit.

Others from the neighborhood came by and we sat outside, wondering what happened. My daddy and momma, ran down the street because all they heard was that somebody got shot. They were nervous, scared that it was me. They were relieved when they saw me. "I'm alright mom. I'm alright dad." It was a sad moment, really a sad moment. I had seen a lot of dead bodies and watched several cats die. I had a couple of partners die. But to see bullets hit this innocent boy, to see him fall down, and how scared he was. To watch him ask God to spare him, and to see God take him in his hands through a woman who was praying, was amazing to me. I didn't know how God worked. But at that moment I looked up and thanked the Lord, "Thank you, Lord. You got my attention.

Just a week ago, I was laughing at You, talking about You, mocking Your name, Your students, Your servants, Your messengers. I was in your house mocking You."

God had my attention. I understood that God had his arms around me my entire life. At the age of 11, I had gone to the doctor because my mouth was swollen and it was hurting. I had just been to the dentist to get my tooth filled. We went back and forth getting it fixed. My mom rushed me to the doctor. As soon as I got there the abscess in my mouth burst. The poison went through my system right at the hospital. I had died in that hospital but they brought me back. I woke up under a cold blanket to keep my temperature down.

God really had his arms around me. Another time during my youth, I hopped over a fence that my daddy warned me not to hop over. A nail was sticking out of a stick about five inches. I slid down the fence and my eye got hung on the nail. I was hanging on the stick. My feet were dangling, arms dangling. They had to pick me up off the stick. Luckily, I didn't lose an eye. I didn't lose anything.

All these memories were rushing through my head, and I knew God has His arms around me. "I'm sorry Lord. I didn't know. I'm sorry!"

I fell asleep behind the wheel driving down the 91 freeway getting off on Santa Fe. The last thing I remember was being on the 91 headed west passing the 605. When I woke up, I was going off the side of the freeway toward a brick wall 5 feet or 10 feet away. The truck just stopped.

"Wow, wow, God. You got your arms around me." After all this time, I got what the pastor was saying. From this point on I told myself I would give my life to the Lord. I felt this in my heart and soul. I really meant it, but still didn't know his word. After realizing what He did for me, and realizing that He saved me, I still didn't know his word. I still didn't have a relationship with Him. God opened up the door, and I didn't know how to walk in. Besides simple prayers, I

Chapter 18

wasn't able to communicate with God. I wanted to know God. I wanted Him to know me.

Later that night, the call came in that our homeboy had died. His chest filled with blood, drowning him. I was back at home, thinking, "I should be dead right now. It could've been me." It was strictly by the grace of God that my life was saved. It taught me to thank God for all the things that He had done for me, all that He had brought me through, and all the times that He had saved me.

Readers, reflect over your life, listen to my story. Reflect over your life, all of the dangers that you have been through, and if you don't know God, listen to me clearly. If you do not know God, He is real. Just look over your life. If you're out here gangbanging, look how many times bullets have passed you. Look how many times you were blessed not to take a bullet. If you're out here selling dope, look how many times you were on that street corner, look how many times you had that sack in your hand. Look how many times you could've been dead. If you're out here hoeing, look how many times you had sex without a condom. Look how many times you were just out here wilding out. If you're in these strip clubs, look how many times you were stripping, Look at all the wild threesomes and orgies and parties you had. Just look at what goes on in your life. If you've been out here in this world living wrong, living foul, just stop for a minute and reflect on

I Don't Want To Die Lord

your life and thank God. You, you my friend, you homie, you my sister, you, you, reading this, you were me. Look at me, you were me. We aren't supposed to be here, but by the Grace of God look at us. Look at us. We're here, we're here and we're strong. Listen to these words as I'm talking to you. Reflect for a second and just thank God. I'm thanking Him in the name of Jesus, Lord I thank you Lord, thank you Father.

I went down the street the next morning to replay the night before. There had been drive-by's in the hood, but never on this street.

Over the next few weeks, I reflected over my life and just how crazy it had been to that point. It was crazy. The bloods and crips were feuding, gangbanging, shooting back and forth.

Around September, October they let one of my little homeboys have it. "Little E just got shot!" We were outside trying to figure out what was going on. I remember the Feds just creeped up behind me, "What's up?" I turn around. He said, "Yeah, how you doing?"

"Who are you?"

"I'm the Feds that's on your case. Blake."

I looked at him gritting.

So you plan on going to trial, huh? Don't do it, don't go to trial. Your little six year old, your little son, your daughter, you know your little girl. She's about four? And that one in

169

your wife's stomach. She ain't your wife, but in your girl's stomach."

I thought, "Damn, how he know this shit?" Deborah was pregnant again at the time.

"Yeah, don't do it, don't go to trial. They don't want you. They don't even know about you. They just slipped up on you. But don't go to trial. I got all of them. I got the best of them."

He started naming people who got 20 years, 25 years, 30 years, that had been in the game.

"Don't do it. Just ask around. They all know me. I've been a Feds for 19 years. I'm telling you, if you go to trial I will see to it that your little boy, will about 16/17. Your little daughter will be about 14. Your unborn son, the one in her stomach, will be about 12, 13. I will see to it that you get at least 19 years."

I just walked away, tripping off the dude wondering how this mothafucka just read my life story in a nutshell. If he knew this bitty shit, what else do he know?

The next day I got a call from my attorney, "K you know you have to come down here."

"What's up?"

"I need you to come down here."

When I got there, he told me that they had a witness that I sold them drugs. I hadn't been selling any work, so I

I Don't Want To Die Lord

couldn't figure out who it could be. I made a few phone calls and wasn't nobody caught up. "Whatever," I thought.

My attorney said it just changed the chances to 50/50 from 80/20. I couldn't gamble with 50/50, not with my life. I asked him to wait till we got some more evidence. I know what we had, but we were supposed to be getting some more discovery, tapes, more things to listen to.

Chapter 19

You Have To Trust Me

2 Pac was killed. The homies came to the hood that day. They were celebrating, "Homies just got Pac, homies just got Pac!"

"Y'all the man now. Y'all done put in a lot of work, but y'all ain't never killed a celebrity. Y'all the man now dude."

The next day, the Feds were all in Compton, in the hood. I left to go to my other spot where Deborah was. I didn't want to be close to the Feds. The hood was hot from the Feds and the police, but the bloods and crips were at it too. They were out there laying each other down left and right. Another one of my homies was killed during that time! They had mistaken him for another cat. He had just dropped his son off at school, backed up, and little youngsters hit the corner and laid him out right in front of his house. This dude was a bodyguard, good working dude, nothing to do with this.

I felt like everything around me was crumbling. Everything was crazy. The neighborhood was crumbling, Feds were all in the neighborhood now.

I got my court date in February 1997. At my first hearing, the judge ask the prosecutors what kind of evidence they had. The prosecutors presented a wire taps for everyone involved. The judge said, "That's it? You don't have any drugs, or money?"

"Yes."

"You'd better make sure this wiretap is clear! Or we're not even letting this in the courtroom!"

That was my first victory. They rescheduled us to come back in April.

With all the madness in the streets, I decided to start selling all my possessions to make sure I was alright. I had some money put up. I didn't need all these cars. There was a pretty good chance that I was going to jail. If I didn't go to jail, I could always repurchase those things. In the meantime, I had a substantial amount of money put away for Debra and the kids.

One day, Deborah was sitting at our house in Compton, just crying. I told her, "You know what babe. I don't know how much I'll get, but right now I'm facing 10 years. So you know just go on about your life. Go live your life. Don't even worry about me. I'll be alright."

"That's fucked up that you would say that. Where I'ma go? I ain't went nowhere all these years. Where I'ma go? I don't want to go nowhere. I want to be here with you."

10 years is a long time. Would she really wait? I don't know. I'm one of them cats that, if you tell me you gonna do something, you do it. It's not that I'm controlling or anything, but my woman ain't gone be running the streets out wilding out.

"This is what we gone do," 'cause I know me. I know my heart. If you got my heart I could be hurt, if you don't then no big deal.

"It's two ways I'll do this time: With you- or without you."

"What does that mean?"

"Anything you've been doing before I leave, you keep doing. If you start changing and things start changing then we ain't gotta be together. It's that simple. If things start changing I'ma let you go."

Now what people fail to realize out here is when you love somebody, you love 'em. So I don't care where they are, when they leave you. It's not a physical leaving you. it's a spiritual, mental leaving you. You're tearing yourself apart from that person. So that pain is still there. I explained that to her. "If you start changing, I'm done. That's it."

You Have To Trust Me

She agreed. I let her know that I had money, and would make sure my sister gave her money when she needed it.

"Well Kevin, you know if we gone be together you have to trust me. We had talked about being married. We were supposed to get married. You know you gotta trust me."

She never had that much money at one time. Could I trust her not to run through it?

"How do you know?"

"You're right, Deborah. I don't know. I'll make sure you're all right."

I made sure I set everything up so she could be all right, but remaining realistic.

During the last court hearing, the judge accepted the wiretaps. Time went by and the next court date came up in May,'97. At the court hearing we listened to the judge tell us what we were being charged with. I hadn't made a plea agreement since I was still thinking about going to trial. After the trial, I discussed the case with my attorney, "Their informant is saying I sold them drugs and I don't think that's true. Can they use my co-defendant, even though he had already plead guilty? He had plead guilty since he had a case in Tennessee or Memphis. Could they use his testimony against me?" My attorney said yes.

"You basically don't have too much longer before you plead out. You know they're offering you a deal for 70 months. That's almost 6 years."

Chapter 19

I could live with that. He said it might change. We had to meet with the Feds for this plea agreement and I really didn't wanna go down and meet with the Feds. I waited until 10 minutes before the deadline to meet with them. My oldest sister D, Deborah and I went down there. During this plea agreement, we went before a board. This board happened to be a female agent and two male agents, my attorney, my sister, and Debra. We were sitting in a room and they asked questions like, "Do you know this cat? Do you know that cat?"

"No, I don't know this cat. I don't know that cat."

"Do you know about what's going on in the streets?"

"I don't know nothing that's going on in the streets."

"What is your involvement in this case?"

Mind you, this case is from my robbery.

"Look man, I don't know. I got robbed and that's all that I know. I looked outside and they were beating this dude and I got robbed. I don't know what else. I don't know nothing else."

I kept telling them this.

"This isn't the story we want to hear, Mr. H"

"It ain't no story. That's the honest truth. I got robbed, and outside of that, I got robbed."

They didn't like it. They continued to ask me about different cats. I continued to tell them I didn't know them.

You Have To Trust Me

"Look dude, I'm going to tell you like this. You're asking me about a rumor, some stuff that I heard. I can tell you a whole bunch of stuff that I heard. I can tell you about a whole bunch of rumors. But who in this room right now has never had a rumor spread on them that wasn't true?"

The female officer, the agent, started laughing. One male agent got so mad he turned beet red. He was pissed. We went back and forth, back and forth.

"Well Mr. H, you know. We know that you haven't been selling dope in the last 16 months per our informant so we're going step out of the room and see what we're going to do."

They stepped out of the room and talked it over. My attorney asked me why I was so hostile.

"What do you mean 'why was I so hostile?' this is my life you're talking about. They're talking about giving me ten years. I'm not telling them nothing!"

My sister D asked me to calm down.

"I'm not calming down, man. This my life. How am I'm going to be calm when they're talking about giving me 10 years for nothing. I'm not being calm."

Debra tried calming me down. They couldn't calm me down. Shit I was mad.

"What the fuck I'ma calm down for when you talking about giving me 10 years that I got to do? Calm the fuck down, noooo. Ain't no calming down."

So they came back in the room.

Chapter 19

"We really don't want to give you this safety vow."

A safety vow gives you 2 points off for being a first time offender. I was at a level 32 for being charged with conspiracy with intent to distribute 6 kilos of powder cocaine.

The Feds are different from the state. With the Feds, there are guidelines. You get caught with this, you do this; you get caught with that you do that; you get caught with this you do what the guidelines say. It's black and white.

"Okay, shhhh." Hopefully now I could get boot camp. I would be home in a matter of maybe three-four years. After the safety vow and all this mumbo jumbo, first time offender, whatever, my charge went down to a level 27 which gave me a 56 month minimum, 72 months max.

My attorney discussed the process with me. I still had to be sentenced. We went back to court to make my plea. *Guilty of Conspiracy With Intent to Distribute 6 Kilos of Powdered Cocaine.* Whatever they didn't charge me with, they couldn't bring it back up. They couldn't charge me any time in the future. I was nervous. I didn't know if they were going to keep me that day. That judge was mean, especially when it came to drug dealers. The judge read what we asked for: Sentenced to a camp, minimum security, boot camp. The judge granted everything that we asked for and then he asked if there was anything else.

"Yeah. My attorney won't say nothing, so, your honor, can I speak?"

You Have To Trust Me

"Yes, Mr. Hawkins"

"Well, I would like to stay out on bail."

"Why is that Mr. Hawkins?"

"My son is due to be born in July, so I would like to stay out to see my son born. I understand I made a left turn instead of making a right turn and I accept full responsibility, your honor. I just want to stay out to see my son being born then I can go get my life back together."

"Okay. Is there anything else that you want?"

"Yeah, I would like to go to Vegas and get married."

He just started laughing. The whole courtroom basically laughed.

"You've been with this girl all this time, and have two children with her and one on the way. Why haven't you married her?"

"Your honor. I messed up in my life. I made the wrong turn, you know. I don't have a reason why I didn't marry her. I've been out here wilding out."

"You have a good woman. I'm surprised she's still here with you."

He granted me the time to stay out. Everybody was in awe. That was a unique day.

We left the courtroom, my girl was happy, my family was happy though I'm guilty though now. I just had to do my time.

Chapter 20

My Legs Buckled

I had never been to prison. Walking out of the courthouse, I thought about how my life was about to change. My brother was in Lompoc at the camp. A memory came to me of a particular day going to visit him at the camp. They had the FCI up there, which was the low. They had the high. The Lifer's were in the high. Barbed wire surrounded this prison, along with tall gun towers. The place looked like death.

I was nervous about going to jail, and that memory didn't help. While out on bail, I was riding my Harley, still living. It was a whole new way of living for me. I was enjoying myself

My Legs Buckled

on my hog now and sold all my cars, letting time go by. I was anxious for my son to be born because I wanted to get this over with so I could go back to court. The judge had postponed my sentencing date to August 1st.

My son was born June 12, 1997. I had a few weeks to spend with him and we still hadn't gotten married. We finally went to Vegas on July 31st. Deborah, my sister D, and I went up there. Deborah and I got married at the little white chapel in Vegas. We came back August 1st and went to court the next morning. I was sentenced to 72 months. My brother, in Lompoc was out by now. He was there along with my younger brother, my momma, my daddy, my wife, and my sisters. They sentenced a few people, then,

"Ummm Mr. H."

"Yes your honor." My attorney and I stepped forward.

"Ummm Mr. H under the law of the Federal government, we are sentencing you to 72 months."

My brother was in the back, "Yesss!"

I calculated, 72 months, 12 months in a year so pssst, psst, pssst, umm,umm,ummm,umm, "Fool that's 6 years!" My legs buckled and my brain went numb. "I can't do this," was all I could think. I was trying to be strong.

Right after the sentencing they get everyone up out of there. My family walked out of the courtroom. I didn't drop any tears, trying to be tough. After my family walked out the courtroom, the marshals walking me with handcuffs. As soon

181

Chapter 20

as my family walked out of the room, I broke down in tears. The only thought going through my mind was, "I can't do this."

They walked me into the hall. My family was still out there and my wife screamed. That shit fucked me up. They rushed me on the elevator, on down to processing. Once the processing was complete, I was a convicted felon, a convicted drug dealer. I sat in the holding tank, all day waiting for court to be over so they could transport everyone at once. They took us back up to MDC where they threw us a nice little spread. I guess this was our welcome back celebration.

D was in there talking shit, about whatever he was going to do to me. Somehow he pulled strings and got me in the same room. They looked at me and thought it was going down. "What the fuck they looking at?" I thought. I, grabbed my shit, put it on the bunk and everything was cool. We chopped it up that night.

"Man, you know I know what happened. You know I seen the paperwork. I just want you to know that." He couldn't say anything so he just sat there ignored what I said. Now that we were both in jail, there was no need to be mad or hold animosity and shit towards one another. He knew what happened, I knew what happened and it was done with as far as I was concerned. I wanted him to know how scandalous that shit was that he tried to pull. If I were some

182

My Legs Buckled

punk ass, sucka ass nigga he would have got away with that shit. But, fuck it. This was my first night in jail, starting a 72 month sentence. With good time, good behavior, and all that shit, mothafucka might be out in 5 years. Fortunately, at the time of sentencing, the judge gave me boot camp which gave me 18 months more off my sentence. That brought it down to only 4 years, or 3 years and some months. I was to go to Boron, a camp for first time offenders, under ten years with a nonviolent offense. In the meantime, I was in MDC.

My stomach was all fucked up. I had been trying to hold out on going to the shitter, but it didn't work. I had to use the bathroom! The cell was a two man cell with a bunk bed, sink and bullshit ass mirror made out of kind of sheet metal and toilet. At about 2 AM, before we finish chopping it up, a nigga had to take a dump.

"Fuck, man. I have to use the bathroom."

"Nigga, you better get used to this shit cause you ain't gone never get privacy while you use the bathroom. You know just go on over there and handle your business."

As I used the bathroom, the shit start stinking. I got my first rule of thumb, "Dump one, flush one."

"Nigga what's that?"

"When you dump one you flush one."

So I dumped one, flushed one, dumped another, flushed another, etc. "Ain't this a bitch. Here I am in the fucking bathroom, using the bathroom in front of another fucking man."

I dozed off for the night after that. They crack the doors at about 6 o'clock in the morning to use the phone. We had to sign up to use the phone. We were allowed to put our names on the list 3 times throughout the day in 15 minute increments. As soon as sign I signed my name, I got ready to stand in line for breakfast. This is the morning routine I followed until I went on to my destination, Boron. I called my wife, talked to her about the first night and asked how the kids were doing. Everything was fine.

I explained the dump one, flush one and made her laugh. I called my moms and my after her and let them know I was alright. I went through the day feeling sick to my stomach still. In MDC there are nine floors called dorms. On each floor there could be a pool table, or ping pong table. There's a small basketball court and weight bench on the outside deck. When I got bored, a nigga shot some pool for about a hour. I didn't know how to do time, so I just kept myself occupied.

This was the routine over the first week. I saw my wife and parents during this time. My wife wanted to bring the kids but I told her no. I really didn't want them to see me like this, not in this environment. There were a series of metal detectors, and searching just to get in. That wasn't the environment for kids.

184

My Legs Buckled

The second week come around and I played some dominos, and cards. My partner told me that the worst thing to do in jail was gamble and play board games. Those started the biggest fights because the inmates couldn't handle it the loss. With my mouth, I tried to stay away from the board games.

But I played pool. I was on the table whippin' this nigga's ass. He got all salty, trying to gamble me. I wasn't about to gamble in jail. We played for some little bullshit ass pushups. We almost got into it over that. An older cat who had been down a while, Harry O was watching me. He pulled me to the side. "You a smart little young fellow. I heard a lot about you. You keep your head on your shoulders."

We went into his room, chopped it up. He was schooling me on prison since he'd been down a while. He was a wise brother. He was telling me about the system, his life, things he did, things he accomplished, how he was in the plays, who he dealt with back in the day and some of the names he dealt with. I was impressed.

The people I met inside prison, the first week, opened my eyes to how big the game really is. The Federal government has designed the game for a reason.

I met a Chinese man who owned a bank. He was in prison for tax evasion. Why he should pay taxes in America when he is loaning Americans money made no sense to me.

Chapter 20

But that's how they got him. If you don't play by their rules, they get you.

I met a judge, ex cops, a scientist, the owner of a water bottling company. These were intelligent men. These men became a threat to the system because they raise educated kids who aren't scared of the system and don't listen to what the system says. The government finds ways to stop this breed.

After about three weeks in, a gang of little knuckle head niggas from L.A. caught cases and ended up there. Mothafuckas had been robbing banks and shit so they thought they were hard. I'm a little cat, 5'6" about 120. I was the only one using the phone most of the time around this time. So one youngster came to me and asked, "Man, let me use some of your time for a second homie."

"Sure, okay," being cool. In my book, respect is something that you give, not something that you can earn, or take. It's what you give. "You can have five minutes, but in five minutes, I need the phone."

"Alright, homie. Don't trip."

So I waited. Six minutes went by.

"Hey, holmes. It's a minute past your five minutes so you got to get up off the phone."

"Alright cuz, homie. Just wait a minute homie, cuz just wait."

My Legs Buckled

I was trying to be calm. A couple more minutes went by and he was on my time now. I was being tested now, I could see.

"Hay holmes, dawg. Get up off the phone, man. I let you use 5 minutes and it's 3 minutes past."

"Nigga, cuz, fuck you. Nigga can't you see I said nigga, wait?"

So I went over there and hung the phone up, *click*.

"Nigga, cuz. I'm finna fuck you up, punk ass mothafucka, bitch ass nigga." He as going off on me. I looked at the guards, at my people.

"Don't trip homie, alright? I'ma be that. Don't trip."

He kept running his mothafuckin' mouth. I went over to my cats, "How we do it up in MDC?" The MDC dorms were long, and our rooms were way in the back away from the guards. When we wanted to get down we went back there and handled our business. They made sure everybody was alright. Nobody got stuck up in MDC.

I told my people, "Man, this nigga gonna basically try to punk me for some phone time and he think he can whoop my mothafuckin' ass? I just need y'all to watch my back.

Come on cat. Come on partner. Let's go to the back. Nigga you was just wolfing, nigga. Let's go to the back right now. Cuz, that's right, cuz. Let's go. You ain't got to get loud dawg. It's just me and you right here. Let's go to the back. We do what we do. You whoop my ass, you whoop my

187

ass, I whoop yours, and that's it. Let's just go to the back. We ain't even got to get loud. You ain't got to loud talk me."

So we start walking to the back. He got about five steps in, "Aww, cuz you serious?"

"Man look, don't cuz me homie. Let's go do this, nigga. I let you use my phone time, and you want to play me like some sucka ass, bitch ass nigga. I want you to prove to me that I'm a sucka ass, bitch ass nigga that you was wolfing."

"Aww, cuz, man. It ain't like that."

"Naw it is like that, nigga lets go homie."

His homeboys they couldn't come back there with him. My people were right there so he didn't know what the fuck to do. "C'mon, dawg. Lets just go back here and handle this!"

"Aww dawg."

"That's what I thought. You a little bitch ass nigga, man. Don't come at me like that. Nigga, I'm telling you right now, I let you use my phone time and I probably will let you use it again. But if you ever disrespect me like that again, I'll whoop your mothafuckin' ass. I'm not a bad nigga and I'm not a big ass nigga but one thing I do, I got heart and I will scrap. So I'm telling you homie, I'll shake your hand, we cool, we straight, no love lost. Let's leave this shit alone."

Niggas in there, if they didn't know, now they knew, that this nigga wasn't no punk.

My Legs Buckled

After about four weeks in a mothafucka done got people. Cats were in there playing and wrestling and shit. One day, I was wrestling with this mothafuckin' Asian dude and I got his ass. But man, this mothafucka did a move on me and kind of fucked me up under my arm. My arms got loose. So, fucking with him, I learned a little shit.

It had been four weeks since I had seen my kids. The max I had ever been away from my kids was probably five days. Even when Deborah and I weren't getting along, I still went and picked up my kids. It was killing me not seeing them. Deborah came to visit, and I was looking the best I could in prison. I rode the elevator down, facing the opposite wall as usual so I couldn't see what floor we passed. I'm not sure why they do that, but I assume it's to keep us unaware of our location in case we try to escape. They led me to the visiting room where the visiting tables were located. They told me at which table she was sitting, and I met her. As I walked in, I noticed my daughter there, sitting down with her head on the table, eyes glassy with a sad look on her face. As soon as I saw her, my legs got weak. When I sat at that table and looked in her eyes, I saw her sadness, fear, concern, and uncertainty.

Each night on the phone she asked when I was coming home. She told me she loved me. She didn't understand why I wasn't there, or why I hadn't been around.

Chapter 20

I cried, when I saw her little face. I don't know how many men would feel me, but a lot of you women reading this book will feel me. To be away from my child for so long, then to see her, with all the hurt, the pain, and vulnerability made me feel so helpless. I wept, "Father, Lord. Please watch over my baby. Please."

I couldn't take it. I know I caused the pain. I hurt my baby when I left.

"You alright daddy?"

"Yeah, baby. I miss you. I love you. I miss you."

My wife's intentions were good, but it was hard for me. My daughter wanted to touch me, but the mothafuckin' CO's, bitch ass mothafuckas warned, "Don't touch her. You can't touch her."

"This my baby, my daughter!"

"Ain't no touching in here."

"Fuck, I can't even hold my baby?"

Despite that, we ended up having a good visit. I went back upstairs with an emptiness and a pain in my heart. It was unbearable to leave my daughter. I was fucked up for the rest of the night.

I went in my room, back to my cell, and just laid in bed.

Chapter 21

Trust Me When I Say That

During my stay, I picked up a few books, the bible being one of them. I tried reading a book about a guy going away who saved his family. I pick up another book by Ben Ammi called *God, the Black Man, and Truth*. It gave me knowledge and insight to this world. "God is good. He's beautiful, He's loving." The books were uplifting through the night but when the sun came up, I was back to the same things. *Sign up on the phone list, get on the list, eat breakfast.*

Chapter 21

Along with the regular day, there was some crazy shit that kept people occupied. The women were on the opposite side of the door. This was some of the craziest shit in the world to me. Those fucking nasty ass broads were putting cum in aluminum foil with pubic hairs and sliding it under the door. These mothafuckas were smelling it. I thought, "Y'all some nasty, sick mothafuckas. I don't give a fuck how long you been down, that's some sick ass shit." Whatever you do to make your time go by, to float your boat, that's what you do.

One day I decide to play dominoes this nigga was talking a gang of shit. He was a black ugly mothafuckin' oil-slick-black-ugly-mothafucka. He was out of some hood in L.A. I was wearing his ass out. He got mad and got up yelling and throwing the mothafuckin' dominoes across the table, "Nigga, you think you hard, you bitch ass nigga?"

"Man, whatever."

"Yeah, nigga. I'll fuck you up."

"You threw the mothafuckin' dominos across the table, nigga. You ain't threw me."

"Nigga, keep mothafuckin' talking and I'll whoop your motherfukin' ass."

"But ain't nothing stopping you! Ain't shit stopping you from whooping my ass."

I heard that this nigga was a snitch so the guards had his back. He made a big ass scene. I sat on the mothafuckin'

Trust Me When I Say That

table not really tripping off this nigga. He had a lot of mothafuckin' mouth and my plan was, "*If this nigga rise I'ma hit him so hard in his mothafuckin' throat one good time and cut all that shit out. He won't be talking no more.*"

"Man, nigga. You better shut the fuck up before I walk up in the shower on your ass tonight with baby oil."

He was known for doing that shit in there. They would walk in the shower with baby oil all greased down all on a mothafucka and start trying to rape your ass. I guess that's what they do in here. I hadn't seen it, but I heard about it.

"Tell you what, nigga. This how we gone do this. I'm gone take a shower tonight cause I take a shower before I go to bed. Walk up in my mothafuckin' shower baby oiled down and we gone see what happen. Nigga if I got to scratch, kick, bite, knee, elbow, whatever, me and you gone be in this mothafuckin' shower. Me and you. And I guarantee you that's gone be the last time your mothafuckin' ass walk in a shower with somebody. Trust me when I say that nigga. So do it. I'm gone take a shower. Matter of fact I'm gone get up right the fuck now nigga and go take my shower right now."

And that's what the fuck I did. I got up and took my mothafuckin' shower. I waited for this nigga to walk up in that mothafuckin' shower. As I said before, I'm not bad, trust me, I'm not a bad ass mothafucka. I don't even like to fight. That shit hurts to be honest. But I will fight to defend my mothafuckin' self.

193

Chapter 21

Coming up through elementary and junior high school, a man name Eddie lived on our street who taught marshal arts. After class we were fighting and practicing our techniques. He grabbed me and let his son whoop my mothafuckin' ass. His son didn't even want to do it but his dad was steady, "You better sock him, boom, you better sock him, boom." This mothafucka was socking me, kicking me while I was getting mad and crying and shit.

"Yeah just whoop his ass! That's right!"

After he hit me a few times, I get so mad and angry I just stopped crying and looked at him.

"When your daddy lets me go, I'ma whoop your ass! I'm ma whoop your ass!"

I sat there gritting, telling him I was going to whoop his ass. When his daddy let me go, man, I fucked him up so bad, he started throwing up. That's how he trained us. It taught us how to take punishment and still be focused. We learned not to fear getting hit. It ain't that the average person can't fight, it's that when they get hit they don't know how to take it.

I wasn't tripping if this mothafucka run up in the shower. I just knew that when he came up in there, he better be prepared. I will handle my mothafuckin' business for a little mothafucka.

My hair grew out by this time and I was wearing a small afro. There were some talented cats up in prison. There were dudes that would take a comb and put a straight edge razor between the comb, use that shit like mothafuckin' clippers. Dude gave me a smooth ass haircut, so I let him cut me up once a week so I wouldn't be looking shaky and shit with my fro.

On my 5th week, they were moving people around. I was moved to a floor with nothing but lifers. I found out eventually that this floor was depressing. They were like zombies. When I first came in, there was a cat who got arrested 16 months earlier. He was a cool cat, kind of tall, with a little weight on him. He had caught a case and ended up getting time. When I asked how much time he got, he told me his release date was is 2072. 2072! We were in 1997. **Two-thousand-seventy-two**!! "What the?" That shit fucked my head up when I saw him in there, zombied out. His case was caught in prison when he killed a nigga after being raped by him.

There was a cat in there- bad with the pen. He drew cards- birthday cards, anniversary. I had him draw a card for me to give my wife. It was a nice card. "You ever thought about opening a shop when you get out of here?"

"Man, I'm not getting out. I got double life. I'm in here trying to get a life sentence off me."

I just swallowed my tongue. Here I was with 72 months and this man right here got double life. We started talking and he said, "Man, this floor is for people who got life and

Chapter 21

they're trying to get some time off. You know, they're trying to get back in the system."

Ain't this a bitch.

The little young cats out of L.A. were wilding out on this floor. These mothafuckas were communicating with people through the toilet. They took a magazine, rolled it up, and stuck it in the toilet, yelling through the magazine. They came over to ask me if they could use my bathroom.

"Go ahead."

They entered my room. I didn't have to share the room on this floor, since these were one man rooms. I was just trying to stay out of the way on this floor cause it was kind of crazy. They went in there, hollered at the girls.

"Why the fuck do they have me on the floor with fucking lifers?"

The inmates were asking me how much time I got and I had to tell them I was still waiting to be sentenced. I might gossip, but I wasn't trying to tell these mothafuckas I had 72 months while they were in there with life. That's some depressing ass shit to hear, you know.

"Fuck; they got to get me off this fucking floor."

I met with my counselor, "Y'all got to get me out of here."

"You're going to be leaving in a minute so you will be alright."

"Yeah, I hope I'll be alright, shit."

Trust Me When I Say That

I wasn't trying to catch a fucking case and be up in here for fucking life. I was on a floor with lifers defending my fucking self. Either they were going to take my life or I was going to take one of theirs defending my fucking self.

5 ½ weeks in, one of my homeboys came through on his way out.

"Kevin, wassup?"

"Shit, nothing."

"I'm out of here in the morning. I got one more stop then I'm on my way home."

"Shhh, I wish I could say that."

"How much time you got?"

"72 months."

"How long you been here?"

"Almost 6 weeks."

"It will go fast, dawg. Don't even trip. I been down for almost 5."

Yeah, that shit sounded good, 'cause I ain't never been to jail a day in my life. So these 5 ½ weeks, almost 6 weeks felt like a fucking eternity to me.

I got the call to pack my stuff up. We got ready to go, packed up, and went on my way to the next place before boot camp. We were on the bus ride for a while. We ended up in San Bernardino County. I had never been to L.A. County, but from what I heard, San Bernardino County was worse than L.A. County. When we got off the bus, they had seven feet

Chapter 21

tall, fucking red-neck ass mothafuckin' guards, gritting and talking a gang of shit. As we got off the bus, the lieutenant said, "This is my mothafuckin' prison! Anybody got a problem, we got something for yo ass!"

We went into the holding tank. I looked over and saw this one cat in a tank by himself, naked.

"What the fuck type of shit is this?"

I asked the guys around me, "Man, what's up with dude right there?"

"Aww, man. He's on suicide watch. You know, some people can't take this, so the guards take everything so he won't be able to hang himself, cut his wrist or do no detriment to himself. They put him on suicide watch."

"Damn!"

Over to the corner was a fucking chair with straps like a rollercoaster ride.

"What the fuck is that for?"

"Well, if you get out of line and you start tripping, they strap you in there and beat your ass."

"OK I'm not trying to go through neither one of these."

I went back over to talk to my partners. When we came out of that holding tank we started going to the back to the cells. One fool was trying to gang bang he in there, sagging. The guard came and booted him so mothafuckin' hard in his ass, "You in MY jail in MY house. Didn't I tell you that? Pull yo mothafuckin' pants up!" He grinned, "I'll whoop yo

198

mothafuckin' ass right here! Straighten yo mothafuckin' face up!"

And dude straightened his face up quickly.

"Y'all get out of line, we will fuck you up in here!"

I ain't never seen no white boys this big. Big ass, I mean fucking corn-Feds-ass cats.

The Federal inmates are held in a different place than the state because the Feds contracted us out to the states. The state gets paid more money for us and they keep us separate. In here you see cats all fucking PC'd up. They're in protective custody for possibly snitching on someone you see them with a certain color jump suit on. Mothafuckas with different color tags on have aids or some shit.

They took us to the dorms and it was freezing. Man it was so fucking cold.

"Why is it so cold in here?"

"We got to keep the germs down."

They had metal bunks, with a fucking bullshit ass bottom bed. I was freezing my ass off. I tried to stay warm, but I had no coat, no clothes.

The next morning, I got to use the phone to call my wife and family. After the call, we went down to the chow hall where we all ate by our inmate number. There were signs on the wall throughout, "Don't look up." One cat looked up and the fucking guards yell, "Didn't I tell you! Didn't you see the sign that says when you sit down and eat don't look up?

199

Chapter 21

Look up again, and I'll knock the fucking shit out of you." I made sure I didn't look up. There was no winning there.

This was an experience and a half for my ass. I wondered when I was going to Boron. I was tired of this shit. Boron is a camp with no fences. That's what they were saying. I had never been to a camp. But everywhere I had been so far had bars. After for like 4 or 5 days, I called my attorney to find out if it was something he could do or not. Other cats were calling their attorneys. They scheduled us to be out of here in 6 days.

After the six days they took us from fucking San Bernardino County to Kern County. Man, Kern County is fucked up. It was dorm living with 100 and something niggas, all races, with 3 tier bunks. I had never seen a 3 tier bunk a day in my life with a bed at the bottom, middle and top. You don't want to be in the middle because they have to step on your bunk to get to the top. You don't want to be on the bottom because the man up top or in the middle keeps moving so it wakes your ass up. So I was trying to get on top, but it was first come, first served.

The water there was so nasty it had to sit out for 2 or 3 days before it was drinkable. The best thing was breakfast; they brought a nice cold milk, a sack lunch with an orange, and a bologna sandwich. We kept that shit till after dinner, because breakfast came between 6 and 7:30 depending on where we were. Lunch was around 10:30, 11:00am and

Trust Me When I Say That

dinner was at 5 right after the 4 O'clock count. The 4 O' clock count was when we stood by our bunks so they could do a head count. This is when they find out if anyone escaped.

In the dorm, the TV was located right over the toilet, so while you're shitting, you're looking at mothafuckas looking at you, watching the TV over your head. If you turn your head to the right to avoid it, there are fucking two showers over there. You turn your head to the left, somebody over there is brushing his teeth. So. fuck it, I put my head down and smelled my own shit. After the 5th day they called us for transit

Chapter 22

Trying to Laugh and Not Cry So Much

This time there were fucking women on the back of the bus. I looked back and there were no cute women. They were prison women. They looked like us, raggedy, because we hadn't a shaved or cut. Raggedy as shit. After they were dropped of at their location, we went to a so-called transit where people were coming in from a sort of Con-Air. They came in on a plane and some left on a plane. There were cats going to different places throughout the whole Untied States.

Trying to Laugh and Not Cry So Much

It was like a fucking movie. They had like 20 guards surrounding the plane at about a 50 yard radius with machine guns and shot guns.

"What the fuck am I doing on this bus? What the fuck am I doing here?"

They had this thing called the black box. These must have been some bad mothafuckas because they didn't have regular hand cuffs on. Their faces were in fucking masks like real ruthless criminals.

"What the fuck is this shit? What kind of shit is this?"

They exchanged the criminals. Some got on our bus, some got off.

"When the fuck we going to get to Boron?"

I had been to MDC, San Bernardino County, Kern County and all this time, I was in transit getting to fucking Boron. After another long ride, we go hopped on a smaller bus from another prison. That bus took us to Boron.

The first day at Boron we went through orientation. They told us where we were going to be. They gave us clothes. They had a real mirror at fucking Boron. Try going without seeing yourself for some weeks. I walked over to it, and didn't recognize myself.

"Damn, this is me?"

There was no fence surrounding the compound. Cats had their khaki suits on. I recognized a couple partners out of Compton. I guess they knew I was coming. You know prison

203

talk. Whatever is heard on the streets is heard in prison. For those of you who have never been to prison and are out here running your mouths, prisons do talk.

For those of you who are never coming to prison, don't ever come to prison.

The first night in Boron was beautiful. After six weeks of being locked down, I finally had a sense of freedom. It was a relative freedom. We were in dorms that looked like apartment buildings, four men to a room. We had windows, and could walk around at night. There was no 'lights out at nine' like in the last three places.

My homeboys and I stayed up watching TV all night the first night.

"Kevin, what you doing here? I heard you was out there handling your business. You was out there moving a gang of work."

"Was it all worth it now?"

I sat at the window and I looked up, all night, at the stars. It was so beautiful. Just one of the little things I took for granted. I could see the sky, the moon, and the stars. I was in the dark my whole life, and six weeks of complete darkness had opened my eyes. In the last three places, I couldn't tell night from day or day from night. There was no sense of time or direction behind those walls. Time was just the hands moving on a watch or clock on the wall. It was crazy.

Trying to Laugh and Not Cry So Much

This is what cats do, going in and out of prison, all their lives. This was my first and last time in, so it was unbelievable to me.

The next morning we went back to orientation. They asked us what we wanted to do. What kind of job. We had a choice of working in the field, in the yard, in the laundry. Most of the cats wanted to work in laundry to hustle new clothes and sell them. The cafeteria worked the same way, hustle food and sell it. Every prison has a hustle.

Outside of prison, there are always methods to make money. If you're broke, it's a choice. Being in jail and broke is not a choice. There's not much you can do. I've heard, "A nigga rather be in jail than be broke." But I'm going to tell you dawg, when you in jail and you broke, you in jail and you're broke. There were cats up in here starving. Once dinner is served at 4pm, that's it. Whatever you buy at the commissary is basically it until the next commissary.

I was being tested from the moment I walked in Boron. Once I had gone through orientation, I wanted to work in the laundry room or the kitchen, but those jobs were all taken. The hustling jobs always go first. So my first job was to pick up cigarette butts out of the rocks. I had to get on my hands and knees, walk around and pick up cigarette butts. I don't even smoke. I had two choices- do it, or go to the hole. They threaten with the 'hole' shit all the time. They paid me seven

Chapter 22

cents a fucking hour. Fuck it. I'll pick up cigarette butts for a few hours. It got lonely pretty fast.

I remember my first visit. My wife came up, my kids, my mom, my pops, my sister. At Boron you can have as many visits as you want. It was just a matter of how crowded it was. It was a good visit. The next day I saw my homeboy up out of Compton. We chopped it up for a minute. I saw a couple other cats up out of Compton. We chopped it up for a minute and they put me up on game, how everything goes in there. I thought it was cool enough that I could make the best of it.

It was crazy just figuring jail out. No one knows how to do jail their first time in. It wasn't easy to understand . They had a rec center with pool tables and ping pong tables. They had a hobby craft area to make crafts. They had a bachi court, a weight pile. I kicked it with my partner learning how they do this shit.

Boron is by an air force base. We were in a desolate area, so bomb testings were conducted frequently. The planes flew overhead once in a while. One day, man, this shit was funny as hell. I was fresh in off the street we were walking on the yard and I heard BOOM!!!! I ducked and shit 'cause I didn't know what the fuck it was. Everybody on the yard started laughing. Those sounds come across like gun shots, mothafucka ducked around there all day until I got used to that shit.

Trying to Laugh and Not Cry So Much

I was lonely and missing my wife and my family. All day, I just really wanted to be on the phone with my wife and shit or talk to my family. Everyday, there was a new story about how your wife or girl is going to leave you.

"Sancho and Nacho got your girl."

Sancho is the one who keeps it warm while you gone. Nacho is the fuckah that comes through and grabs your girl and tells you those aren't your kids, that's not your wife, your house and, "Don't call here anymore!"

They had a barbershop up in the prison with a barber and mothafuckas on a Friday night laughing and shit, chopping it up, getting fresh hair cuts. Almost like being in the hood. I went in there to get a cut, and these mothafuckas really living like they were free. I hadn't adapted to that shit. I was getting sick, home sick, and lonely. I was trying to figure it out and it wasn't working. I was trying to laugh and not cry so much. I hadn't shed any tears but inside, everyday I was just dying on the inside.

I was doing my time in there. I went to work, a few hours a day. Some cats hit the weight pile, cats on the track, cats playing racket ball, whatever they needed to do. Some drew, some stayed in the music room. They had the chapel to pass there time. I was so new I didn't really know how to pass my time so just floated around from place to place. I hit the weight pile, I ran on the track a little, went to the chapel, talked to my homeboys, went out to the bachi court. I

Chapter 22

bounced, bounced, bounced. I was losing my mothafuckin'
mind in there. I was losing my mind! There were cats going
to school to get their GEDs. There were cats taking programs.
They had a carpentry program. I spent the first two weeks
getting situated and trying to understand how to do this time.

A job offer came up to work in the laundry room. It was
cool because I really didn't want to be outside picking up
cigarette butts and weeds and shit out the rocks. I got in the
laundry room. Cats were getting their hustle on for new
clothes. Cats like to keep their dignity with clean boxers,
clean t-shirts, clean socks, clean khakis. Khakis were the
uniforms that we wore around the yard. We could wear grey
sweats with white t-shirts. On our visits we could only wear
khaki pants with the khaki shirt but we wanted it to be clean.
We wanted to have nice fresh boots on. They had brown
boots, black boots, brown belts, and black belts. We tried to
be clean when we visited with our family so they wouldn't
worry about us. We had to keep our dignity.

I washed and folded clothes for 500 plus inmates at
Boron. I laughed my ass off thinking that a nigga ain't never
washed no mothafuckin' clothes and come to prison washing
clothes and dirty drawers and socks and t-shirts, folding
them up for mothafuckin' 500 inmates. But I did that shit
knocked it out, and everything was going cool.

Trying to Laugh and Not Cry So Much

A few weeks in and I had only had maybe two visits. I really looked forward to them. I missed my wife, my kids, my parents and brothers and sisters. I missed everybody.

It was our turn to go to commissary one night, and I was in there shopping. One of the officers forgot to give me one of my items. I asked him if I could have one of my items and he told me to step to the side and wait. In the commissary, you ain't really trying to wait to the side or you'll be there all night. After 20 minutes I went to my boss who runs the laundry and helps out at the commissary,

"The officer over here forgot to put a certain item in my bag. Do you mind if you can get it?"

"Kevin, sure go head."

With my easy going personality, I make friends pretty fast. My vocabulary might be crazy, but I've never been dumb. She took a liking to me.

"Sure!"

And she handed me the item.

"Thanks!"

I went back to my living quarter and chilled, watching movies with the homies. The male officer, I mean, this Bitch-faggots-ass-freckle-face-red-head-mothafucka came to the dorm and said, "Kevin. Come outside."

I went out there.

"Didn't I tell you to wait for your items?"

Chapter 22

"Yeah, but you were taking too long so I didn't think it was a problem to go to the other line and get my items."

This dude started talking a gang of shit to me. He was riding me like a mothafucka, in my face.

"Look, when I tell your ass to do something, you do it. Do you understand that?"

"Yeah, you got that."

"No, do you understand what I'm saying? When I tell you to do something, you don't go around my back or go over my head to try to get your items. If I tell you to wait you wait. You do what I say. This my house, you understand that?"

"Man, look. I wasn't trying to go over yo head."

"SHUT UP!"

"Man, why you coming at me like this?"

This nigga was in my face now. I really wanted to hit this man, and I knew he was provoking me.

"Yeah, you think you hard, huh?"

"Man, I don't think I'm nothing. I just wanted my item."

"I said, shut up! Look, keep talking and I'll send you to the hole. I'll ship you away from here. I'll have you so fucked up, so far gone, your family won't see you, won't know where you are, won't know nothing."

Being new, I wasn't sure of my rights. I didn't know what I could say or what I couldn't say. I had heard stories about the system, but most of the stories I heard where about the state. State and the Feds are two different systems, ran two different ways. The Feds have incorporated state criminals for state crimes, there were similar types of mentalities in prison.

He was riding me.

"When I tell you to do something, you do it! Do you understand me?"

"Yeah!"

"When I say to do something, I mean right then. Do you understand me?"

"Man, look. Yeah!"

He continued to yell in my ear.

"When I say something I mean it! I mean, now! You do what I say, when I say it. Don't you ever go behind my back to do nothing. You got me?"

I tuned him out because, at this point, he was in my face so close his nose almost touched mine making me angry and he knew it. He wanted me to hit him, "HIT ME! I'm telling you to hit me!"

"Man, go on. I'm not going to hit you, go on."

I got so angry and frustrated at the fact that I couldn't do anything, that tears filled my eyes. The tears started running down my face and I stood there shaking. It took everything within my power to hold back from hitting this man as he told me I wouldn't see my kids, my wife, my family. Martial arts prepared me for the self control I needed. In my

211

frustration, I gave in, "You're right. You got that. You're right, you're right, you're right, you got that." The cursing and name calling went on for a good twenty, twenty-five minutes and all I could do was stand there and take it.

After he left, I went back in my dorm. I walked in my room, grabbed both bunks, and pulled them down in anger.

"Kevin, just calm down, man. He ain't worth it."

I was pacing and shaking. This was his house like he said, not my house. This wasn't where I was gone to reside for the rest of my life, but if I hit this man, I probably would have ended up spending the rest of my life in there. He tried, but by the grace of God, I was able to contain my self. *All glory to God Who gave me strength that day.*

It was time for another visit. Before the visit, they strip search each inmate. During my search, I peaked through the door to get a look at my family as they were walking in. The guard came out saying, "Man, what you looking at? I know you out here."

"Wait, you don't peak inside this glass, matter fact I'll make it were you don't have your visit. You think you one of them hard asses. What you in here for anyways? You in here for selling dope? What, you some sucka ass mothafucka that's up in here for selling dope?"

"Man, look. If you want to know anything about me, go look at my file."

Trying to Laugh and Not Cry So Much

A counselor happened to be there and he call the guard's name asking, "Why are you talking to this man like this? Kevin you know if you want you can file a complaint on him. It's a BP9."

"Man, I just want to see my family."

The counselor made him back up off me.

I went in and I saw my family. They could tell I was kind of agitated and asked me what happened. I told them about the guard and everything that has been going on. My dad advised, "Son, you know it ain't worth it. Don't let them get to you. You are going to be alright."

I went to the law library and spent a lot of time researching. I had to learn my inmate rights, so I started studying the things I could do and couldn't do. This wasn't going to happen to me any more. I spent hours in the law library, looking at my case. When I was sentenced, I got seventy-two months with eligibility for boot camp. After meeting with my counselor, I found out the boot camp didn't apply to me because I was sentenced to over 60 months. Now I was in a political battle because once the sentence began, the Bureau of Prisons took jurisdiction over the courts. There are no laws with the Bureau of Prisons. They could recommend something but it didn't mean the recommendation would stick since policies and laws kept changing. Inmates are stuck between the systems. Until I researched further, I was lost.

213

Chapter 23

I Hear Her Moaning

Prison life was still a mystery after several weeks. I was shooting pool up in the pool hall. There were other cats in there with as much game as I had. This one Asian cat was talking a gang of shit. We talked shit back and forth. I didn't forget what the cat at MDC told me about staying away from games. I whooped his ass, he got mad, "Man, you got a big ass mothafuckin' mouth on you."

"Man, won't you go on with that shit. You lost. Move, bounce, man."

"Keep talking and I'll hit your mothafuckin' ass with this pool stick."

I wasn't tripping off of what he was saying. I grabbed about 3 or 4 pool balls as he walked toward me. I wasn't about to let him get close to me. If he got to within swinging

distance, he was liable to crack me with his mothafuckin'
pool stick and I really didn't know what type of niggas were
up in jail. I wasn't sure what they were made of. My
homeboys diffused the situation when they saw me pick up
the balls. They talked to him, pulled me to the side and they
told me, "K if you want to get down, you know, y'all can go
to the back on the tennis courts. This is how we get down. At
the tennis courts and the racket ball courts."

"I'm not really tripping, man. If that's what he's trying to
do, we can do that."

We were getting ready to do this shit, but I guess
somebody caught wind and stopped it before it went down.

"Y'all need to talk about this shit. It ain't even worth it."

So we talked

I said, "Look, dude. I wasn't disrespecting you, but you
can't just disrespect me. You talking shit to me, I'm going to
talk shit back."

"Man, I got out of line. I got a little heated, you know
I'm cool."

"I apologize for disrespecting you and using the words
that I use. But talking shit is talking shit. You know where I
come from that's what we do. And where I come from you
gonna be a man about what you do and you ain't gone run
from a battle. You only gone live once. Where I come from,
my daddy raised me that you gone die one time. A man is

Chapter 23

going to be a man. A coward dies a thousand deaths a brave man dies once. You know that's in the word."

The days rolled by and I got into a carpentry class to pass my time. I was working in the laundry, doing carpentry, getting my day full. I was also pulled into the kitchen, working in the dish room. We washed a gang of dishes. I was eating real good up in there. We got to cook our own food. Everything was cool.

There was this cat up in there who had his own refrigerator in there. He wore a black long coat, long beard, black hat. I thought he was a special staff member. He was a unique brother. Nobody really talked to him. I found out later that he was a Rabbi with a lot of power. I heard he sued the BOP for millions of dollars. This man had his own refrigerator. They couldn't touch his food. His people brought in his own food. It was amazing to me that this man had this kind of power.

I was finally starting to joke and laugh things off. Every night after the ten o'clock count., around 10:30 to 11:00pm everybody would rush out to get on the phone. I would call my wife and talk to her. We got into it a couple of times. The devil plays games on our minds. I've been gone for some time now, and I wasn't at home to see what was going on. I didn't know if she was cheating. It was in my head since it was all I heard from others, telling me what's going to go down. I got back to my room and one of my bunkies in my

216

I Hear Her Moaning

room was sitting there crying and crying. One of my homeboys asked him what was wrong.

"That fucking bitch. You fucking bitch!"

I just listened.

"I called her, you know, and I heard a moaning. She was just moaning so I told her, 'Won't you tell him to leave you alone,' and she's like, 'Here you tell him,' and handed him the phone."

"What the fuck?"

All night I was fucked up after hearing that story. *"Damn, man. That's some fucked up shit. I hope my wife don't do that to me."*

I heard stories like that all day. The next day he was just walking around like a zombie. That was crazy that she would be fucking a nigga and then put him on the phone. But that's how it goes in prison. So many cats loose their wives girl. They say most families break up after 5 years. I'm wondered if my family was going to leave me or would it last. That bothered me over the next week, so I discussed it with my wife.

"Kevin, just shut up. I'm not going no where. You know every time you call where I am."

"I know, shit. I'm just mentioning it, you know. It's normal."

I continued my schedule over the next few weeks. In my carpentry class I was learning about building houses. We

217

were puttin' it down in the cafeteria kitchen. Thanksgiving approached. This is would be my first holiday in prison, and away from my family. It was a sad occasion. We cooked a feast in there. It amazes me now when I think of that feast. The inmates did all the cooking. We had cakes and pies, turkeys, ham, chicken, yams, Mac and cheese, dressing, red beans, rice, cup cakes, banana pie, lemon pie, cream cheese pie. Cookies, chocolate cookies, sugar cookies, peanut butter cookies. There was so much food we had a feast out of this world. It was crazy to be in jail and see this. I could see why some cats really didn't have a problem coming back to prison. It wasn't impressing to me, but to others who don't eat like this every day, coming to prison was a feast.

A rumor started that a new prison called TAFT was opening up. It was a new privatized institution. We weren't sure who was going to go. The first load of people they grabbed shipped out to TAFT in December. I was leery after being through MDC, San Bernardino County, Kern County and now Boron. I thought I was safe since my sentencing put me in Boron to do my time.

I'll never forget December 18. It was my sister's birthday. On that day, I was shipped to TAFT. They sent 70 of us. When we got to TAFT, it was a new compound, new facility and held about five hundred and some inmates. There were only about 120 to 140 cats after our bus load arrived. There were dorms on top and bottom on one side, top and bottom

I Hear Her Moaning

on the other side. The buildings are building A, building B, building C, and building D. They spread all of us throughout these buildings. In a new facility, with hardly any inmates, it was hard to find anything to do. I was getting sick as the days went by feeling lonely and miserable. There was no recreation. We were in the middle of the dessert. At least at Boron they had grass, even though we couldn't walk on it. We would be sent to the hole for walking on it. The grass had more rights than we humans did. TAFT was all dirt. There was no life.

I laid in my bunk each and every night going crazy. I didn't even want to take a bath, I was so miserable. I had a bible but I didn't read it. I floated day to day once again. Four months had now passed since my incarceration. I had sixty eight months to go. I immediately wanted to vomit thinking about that.

"Lord I can't do this."

I put my head under the cover, laid down and went to sleep. I didn't want to get up the next day. TAFT was so new, they didn't do a stand up count, so I just laid in bed all day.

"Kevin, you can't do your time like this. You know you got to do something," I told myself

I went to apply for a job. I got a job in the kitchen. The prison offers different pay grades. The Kitchen starts off at $16/month, then goes up to $20, $30, $40 $50, $60/month. I worked my way up to about $60 a month. I was establishing my new daily routine, running on the track, doing my push ups, talking to my buddy, getting my visits here and there. The visits were difficult since, once the visit was over, it was sad knowing I had to go back to prison. It was a high and a low. I was still learning how to do the time. I didn't have a relationship with God, so I had no peace. I didn't have books. I had no outlet. I was stuck in prison.

God had his arms around me. Something was telling me to start learning the bible. I went on my journey to understand this. I never read the bible, and never understood it. Picking up the bible, the first section I read was proverbs 1, verse 20- 33, which speaks about wisdom.

(Some Bibles read different)

Wisdom shouts in the streets where ever crowds gather, she shouts in the market places and near the city gates as she says to the people how much longer will, you enjoy being stupid fools won't you ever stop sneering and stop laughing at knowledge listen as I correct you and tell you what I think, you completely ignore me and refuse to listen you rejected my advice and paid no attention when I warned you, so when you are struck by some terrible disaster or when trouble and distress surround you like a world wind. I will laugh and make fun you will ask for my help but I wont listen, you will search but you wont find me, No you will not learn, you refuse to respect the lord, you rejected my advice paid no attention to my warning, now

I Hear Her Moaning

you will eat what you have done until you are stuffed full with your own scheme, sin, and self satisfactions brings destruction and death stupid fools. But if you listen to me you will be safe and secure with out fear of disaster.

Wisdom speaks to us in all kinds of ways, through people of knowledge. There were those who tried to tell me to stop selling dope. I didn't listen.

"Wisdom, is that you talking to me?"

At this point, I think she was laughing at me because I was in prison looking like a fool. It was deep to hear God talking to me. I still didn't know what was going on. It said "You will eat the fruit of what you have done."

The bible mentioned reaping what you sow. I read about sin and self satisfaction bringing destruction and death to stupid fools. I was that fool. I had been out there a fool. A fool in the streets. I started going to church to hear those words. Chapter one, verse 20-23 the spirit was opening up the word to me. "If you listen to me, you will be safe and secure of fear and disaster."

"Wow. What can I do to listen?"

I knew I needed to start listening to the word. I went through proverbs. That was my beginning of understanding God. Every night, I dedicated at least 10 minutes to reading the bible. I called my sister and I had her send me different books. I needed an outlet and that's how I was learning to do time. It took four months of learning to understand the message being given to me.

When I first started doing time we got this thing called pre-trial services. During pre-trial services we're asked different questions about what we plan to accomplish while in prison. I didn't understanding what they were asking. What I did want understand was politics and economics. I wanted to become a better person. I didn't like who I was. I wanted to grow and become something, but I did not know what I wanted to become.

"What is it that I want? What do I want to become? What is it? What am I missing in my life?"

I had a lot of unanswered questions that needed answering by me. I didn't have an answer. I read and learned and grew in prison.

Christmas came around and I was really sad. There weren't many of us in there, and the feast wasn't the same as in Boron. We made the best of it. We ate, we called the family, we said our Merry Christmases, I got a visit. I still didn't understand.

Each week, they would bring in more bus loads of inmates. One cat came in who had done 13 years. This is the first inmate I spoke to, outside of the lifers, who had done so much time. I asked him how he did his time.

I Hear Her Moaning

"You want to know how you do this time? You take it one day at a time, day by day, you walk real slow and you drink a lot of water."

From that conversation, I finally got it. I finally understood how to do time.

"You about to be on a journey so don't over exert your self because this is going to be a journey and a path that you can't move too fast in, 'cause it's one day at a time, one second at a time, one minute at a time, one hour at a time. And if you think about how a day is- it's twenty-four hours. That's a lot of time, and sixty seconds in a minute, its sixty minutes in an hour, there's twenty-four hours in a day."

Day by day. I was going to do it. I wasn't sure how but I was going to figure it out.

In prison, they put us through a psychiatric evaluation. We had to meet with a psychiatrists at MDC when we came in. They gave us an AIDS test. When I took my AIDS test, I was so scared and nervous. It was such a relief to get it back, negative. Since TAFT was my final destination, I met with a psychiatrist who asked some of the dumbest questions that one could ever possibly think of.

"Mr. H how are you doing?"

" I'm fine."

"How are you adapting?"

"I'm not."

"How are you getting along here?"

Chapter 23

"I'm getting alone fine with every body, but I'm not adapting to this place. What kind of question is that, 'How am I adapting,' or, 'how are you handling it?' I'm not handling it. I don't like it."

"Are you having suicidal thoughts?"

"No I'm not having suicidal thoughts. Let me ask you a question. Let me take you away from your mom, from your dad, from your kids, from your wife, from your brothers, from your sisters. Let me take you away from every thing that you've ever been around. I'm twenty-six years old and I'm in prison. I just turned twenty-seven, I've never been in prison a day in my life. Let me take you away from everything that you love and then ask you, 'How do you feel?' I'm not crazy. I'm not having suicidal thoughts. But I'm sick. I don't like it here. I'm sick."

"Mr. H, get out of here."

"Ok cool."

That was the last time I saw a psychiatrist or got an evaluation. I was lonely, mad, and sick. And I was just beginning to understand

Chapter 24

With All Your Heart You Must Trust The Lord

Time went by at Taft. This was camp. The cats that had been down a while and had been to the other camps would ran out to the fields fucking having sex. A couple cats went to the motel. They tried getting me to go but I wasn't doing that. They would put dummies in their bed, and sneak out. One cat was gone for three or four days before they figured it out.

Chapter 24

1998. That summer and they started a basketball league. I got on the team. We played ball, competed with each other. They had softball games going. They finally got the recreation area up. They put in pool tables; there I was playing pool again. One officer got mad and said something to me and after I left, "Yeah, that little colored kid right there." One of my homeboys told me. After being in the law library learning my rights, I knew what I could and couldn't say. I walked up to him and said, "What is my name, sir?"

"What?"

"What is my name? Read my badge," and I put it in his face, real close, and he got scared.

"Look, you called me a little colored kid. I'm not a little colored kid. My name is Kevin Hawkins."

"Well, I didn't know your name."

"You should have asked me my name, the way I asked you."

"Well, I'm sorry."

Earlier that week I was going to commissary and they let this white guy shop in front of me, but they didn't let me shop. I went to the warden, "Hey, warden. You know, I'm kind of nervous at your facility cause I'm being discriminated against at the commissary and I wanted to let you know about it. One of your officers called me a little colored kid. I'm kind of scared for my life. Is there something I should be afraid of? You guys are out of Texas,

With All Your Heart You Must Trust The Lord

you know, and a lot of your guys are, no offense, red necks. I've been called 'colored kid', 'boy' and I'm kind of scared."

So he went to the officer and checked him cold. He was suspended and everything. So, we do have certain rights as inmates in prison.

The first year of prison went by this way. I made it through '98. One year down.

"If I do this again, I'll have two years in."

When '99 came, I started thinking *2000, 2001, 2002. Four more years.*

"Once I make it through '99 I'll have two years in."

This was how I was thinking I was doing my time. Over the first year, I accumulated some books. I read one book called *Our Daily Bread*, by Thomas Nelson. It was feeding my soul, and helping me to understand God. I was beginning to see how He works. I continued to read the bible at least 10 minutes a night. I started in Genesis and went all the way through Revelations. I began to study the questions they asked at my arrival; What did I want? I wanted to become a man. I read books by Ben Ammi, *God The Black Man And Truth*. I read *Nile Valley Contributions To Civilization*, by Anthony T. Browder. I read *Vision For Black Man* by Na am Akbar. As I read these books, I felt myself grow.

There was a place in prison called Unicore. It is a division of the government where products are manufactured. We had the potential to make the most money in Unicore.

Chapter 24

They made a list of about 70-80 people. I made it toward the end of the list, so I didn't make the first pass to Unicore, but I made the second pass. I worked there making chairs and building cartridges. I was responsible for the fabric on the chairs. I made it to grade one making two to three hundred dollars a month. It doesn't sound like much, but in prison $200/month was equivalent to making $80,000 a year outside. Our spending limit was only $285 a month, and my family sending me money, so I was doing alright. There were still some cats in there who were really broke. Like I said before, being broke in prison ain't no joke. That's the bottom line.

I was starting to understand how it worked. I looked back over my life, understand the things that wisdom said. She's talking to me in proverbs. *"If you listen to me you will be safe and secure without fear of disaster."* Proverbs chapter 3 verse 5-7 says, *"With all your heart you must trust the Lord, and not your own judgment. Always let Him lead you and He will clear the road for you to follow. Don't ever think that you are wise enough."*

With all your heart, you must trust the lord.

Readers, if you don't know God, start reading the word. Go to proverbs, understand proverbs. Proverbs is an easy read. Pay attention, again, *"With all your heart you must trust the Lord and not your own judgment. Always let Him lead you and He will clear the road for you to follow. Don't ever think that you are wise enough."*

228

With All Your Heart You Must Trust The Lord

I had been into this word now for a good solid year. I realized that when I was out there in the game, selling dope, pushing this work, I thought I was smart, wise, bright, making a gang of cheese. Women were out there selling their bodies, others were running credit card games, counter-fit money, and we all thought we had it all figured out. Don't ever think that you are wise enough. In other words, don't ever think you are smart or better than God. Always respect the Lord and stay away from evil. That will make you healthy and Strong. Honor the Lord by giving him the first part of your crop, then you will have more grain and grapes than you will ever need. Honor the Lord. He will provide for you. Trust Him. Give Him His, and He will give back. Giving can mean helping others, not just giving to the church. It could be giving knowledge to someone. Readers, don't think you can out-smart the Feds. Don't think you're wise enough my brothers and sisters. The Feds are slick. They have computers and technology.

Here's something real cold y'all. We call them 'snitches'. They ain't 'snitches' my brothers and sisters- they are Feds. Once a person snitches, he or she gets paid. At that point he or she is no longer a snitch- He or she is a Federal agent. The Feds have the game sewed up. You may think you're ducking and dodging them, but you're not getting away with anything. Let me break it down to you, how the Feds work.

229

Chapter 24

The Feds work the way the number counters at the stores work. Everyone has a number. If you pull out of the game before they call your number, you're ok. Every number is called. A lot of you cats out there already have indictments on you. You're free in the streets but you're already in prison. This goes for the dope game, credit card game, counterfeit money game, and the pimp game, to name a few. For y'all out there pimping, man, they got some shit out there for your ass. Pimping is called white slavery. You can get 12 - 13 years for that. Don't think you're wise enough.

The Lord will talk to you. He will tell you, "My child. Don't turn away or become bitter when the Lord corrects you." The Lord corrects everyone he loves, just as parents correct their children. In these pages, I'm not trying to correct you. Don't get mad at me if you're reading this. Brother, I got caught just like the millions of other cats that have been caught. They don't tell you the stories of the ones that got away. There is a very small percentage of the ones who get away. The majority of us don't. They made the rules to this game. They made the laws to fit them. So when the Lord is correcting you, don't get mad don't get bitter. Just listen to His word. Pick up His book if you can, and understand His word. If you plan to stay out there and hustle, do what you got to do in these streets, then I advise you go get a book called *The Federal Sentencing Guideline Handbook*, by Roger W. Haines, Jr., Frank O. Bowman, III, and Jennifer C.

With All Your Heart You Must Trust The Lord

Woll. That book will give you the sentencing limits on certain crimes.

Don't trust lawyers. Don't lean on them for understanding. They are about one thing. When I got caught up, my attorney told the prosecutor, "Hey, I'll meet you on the golf course later on today." Lawyers, prosecutors, judges, defense attorneys, criminal attorney, prosecuting attorney, all came from the same school. Your attorney is not your friend. They constantly change cases, so depending on if they want to take your number, you may be shuffled around. That's how it works. Don't tell your attorney anything. Many cats are in prison because their attorneys sold them out. How did the prosecutor know about something you told your defense attorney? There's a thing called pillow talk and it's dangerous. A man who gets hold of some good loving doesn't know how to handle himself, and starts running his mouth. That's how it goes in the streets and that's how it goes in the legal profession. No amount of money will set you free. *The Federal Guideline Handbook* will tell you exactly what you get for the crime you are accused of. If it doesn't match, you should question what you are accused of.

The things I heard in prison were funny. A cat will tell you he got caught with seven keys of heroine and only got 55 months. Either he told on a gang of people, or he's telling a big old lie. In the Feds it's *Be Who You Can Be*. Another cat said, "I had to go buy some tires for my jet. I'll send my wife

231

to go buy the tires for my Lanier jet." We laughed. Another cat said, "I own a bank up outta here." You hear some funny stories in jail. One homosexual cat in jail said, "I'm gay and I don't even like jail." Jail should be a gay man's heaven.

I went through changes that first year, growing, maturing, becoming a man. Unfortunately I had to go to prison to learn this, but God had to sit me down. They say that God will get your attention some kind of way. If He has to take you to your lowest state, He'll get your attention. He surely got mine.

Throughout 1999, I was playing basketball, running on the yard, staying in shape, getting my workout on. I was in there still complaining about my time. I met another cat who had been down about fifteen years, "Kevin, when you gone stop complaining? When you just gone shut up and do your time? You not getting boot camp. You not going home. You done wrote the judge, and he ain't responded. You in the BOP man. Your time will be a lot easier when learn how to do this time and understand that ain't nothing going to change. You got sentenced to 72 months. With good time after 72 months you going to do 4 years and some months in there. If you get blessed, you can do six months in a halfway house. You have two years in so far. You got 2001, 2002- three more years left. So just ride it out." That was some good advice.

With All Your Heart You Must Trust The Lord

It's a trip that I met good dudes in prison. I learned how to cook using a microwave. We had spreads going on every weekend, cats making pizza, cats making nachos, frying chicken, making mackerel bowls, making some slop, making seafood spreads. There were talented dudes in there. In the music room, there was the live band going on. People were in there   doing   their   thing.

Chapter 25

Whatever You Want for Christmas

I took a course called *Doing and Knowing the Will of God*. It was a terrific program, great course. The instructor was a Chaplain, who, being on the property, was also a guard. The Chaplain and I happened to get into a discussion in class about an issue. He asked if I would allow my kids in the backyard to play if there were quick sand, booby traps, and weeds out there. I said I would. He was comparing the backyard to the dangers and traps of the world. In his eyes, the T.V., certain school functions, and other things, were traps that he didn't allow his children to participate in. I told him that didn't make sense. I asked, "Why wouldn't someone let the kids go out there?" The word says, "Be in the world, but not of the world." We have to live in this world to survive in this world. I explained to him that I would let my kids go in this backyard and play, but not before showing them, "Hey son, hey daughter. That's a quick sand pit over there. Throw a rock in it and watch it sink. Don't go over there. This bush over here, touch the tip. These are thorns and they'll hurt you. Over here live all the scorpions and snakes. Don't go over there. They're poisonous, and will kill you." He disagreed, saying it made no sense.

"You don't let them watch T.V., you don't let them...."

"Hawkins, that's enough."

"We're having open discussion, right?"

"I said that's enough."

"Ok, so now you a cop, huh?"

"Say one more word, Hawkins, and I'll send you to the hole."

Boy I tell you. I didn't say anything. I've prayed a lot for God to give me wisdom, knowledge and understanding of His word, and to bring me into the light of His word. It always comes when it's time for me to shine for His purpose. The word has made me obedient to God. I received it for His purpose to use it according to his will. It was amazing to be able to read books, model after some of these men, and feel this way over such a short period of time. I was able to find peace. I found that peace was attained through my relationship within myself with God. It was a beautiful thing to find him.

As I grew, so did my vocabulary. I didn't curse anymore, stopped using the word 'nigga', stopped being disrespectful. I watched my tongue. The word says that your tongue is like the tool of the sword. It can cut or it can heal depending on how it's used.

We were playing basketball one day. We were out there having a ball. One dude got mad because we were wearing him out, "Nigga, Kevin. You ain't shit, nigga."

"Come on. I ain't 'niggaed' you my brother. I ain't even cursed you."

"Nigga, fuck you, nigga."

"Man, why you going off on me like this?"

"Because, you talk too much!"

Now I still used to talk head but I wasn't cursing.

"You know what, man. We gone have to handle this 'cause you can't keep talking to me like this, naw."

"What you want to do? You want to go to the back?"

"Cool."

So we started walking to the back and he said, "Man you serious?"

"Man, look. Like I said. I've never disrespected you. I didn't call you out your name. I'm not your nigga. I'm not your mothafucka. I'm not none of this. So if you could respect me, we cool. If we cool, let's just shake hands and

Whatever You Want for Christmas

walk back over there. If not ,you gone have to come back here and whoop me. Your going' to have to knock me out, because that what it's gonna take. I'm not gone quit."

We shook hands and went back to the court as if nothing happened. Cats thought we were going to scrap but we didn't. When a man recognizes a man he sees before him then he respects that. Like I said, respect is something that you give. You cannot earn respect, you cannot take respect, and you cannot buy respect. If you give respect to another man or woman of God, that respect is given back. Don't ever for once, all you bad, Billy Bob, big wild cowboy, shoot 'em up, bang bang, from the hood cats think that you are going to go out and take respect from somebody. No matter what, the other person might be scared of you, but he or she won't respect you. Jail is jail, so to you guys who think that jail is good, it's a battle that you won't win. It's a battle that you don't want to win.

My daily routine now consisted of working at Unicore, walking back to stand up count, going to dinner, playing basketball, running track, etc. This was every day life. It was so small in there; the outside world had so much to offer. In jail, you pick a routine; cards, gambling, playing ball, running, reading, whatever you need to do. I learned to do my time by balancing out and staying prayerful. I stayed in my word and kept growing and learning.

237

Chapter 25

1999, I was two years in with three to go. I was reading Ecclesiastes Chapter 3 verse 1-8 which talks about how everything on Earth has its own time and its own season. There is a time for birth and death, planting and reaping, for killing and healing, destroying and building, for crying and laughing, weeping and dancing, for throwing stones and gathering stones, embracing and parting. There is a time for finding and losing, keeping and giving, for tearing and sewing, listening and speaking. There is also a time for love and hate, for war and peace.

I looked back at my life at how everything had its own time. The early 90's was my time to be a fool. I was out in the streets a baller. It was just my time. Everything on earth has its own season, and that was my season to be out there, wilding out, gathering all those women. I was pretty much the biggest fool that I could be. I was a young fool, not knowing God. Those of you might know how it feels to walk into a club and be the star. We all have our time to shine. There's a time for birthing and death, and at this point in my life I was being reborn. Death had to take place in order for me to be renewed. I had to kill that old, prideful, me. I killed that man out there in the streets pushing work, pushing dope, playing the counterfeit money game, credit card game, selling guns. It was a long, hard a process. I was two years in and I could still feel a part of that old me trying to breathe.

Whatever You Want for Christmas

Ecclesiastics talks about planting and reaping. Over the years in these streets, I planted seeds. I planted some dangerous seeds; crack babies, hookers, whores. I also planted good seeds; my children, great relationships. I was beginning to reap what I had sewn.

Ecclesiastics talks about *killing and healing.* I killed many relationships. "Lord how am I going to heal these things? How am I going to heal the people's lives that I destroyed?" Those relationships are dead and gone now. I had to destroy the old me. It says destroying and building. How would I destroy this devilish man in me? In order to destroy it, I had to build a righteous man, an upright man, a man for God, a man for peace, a man for love. I had to build a father for the three children whose lives I had pretty much destroyed by walking out of it. I had to think about rebuilding my relationship with them. I had a wife who I walked away from. She depended on me and I destroyed her life. I had to build our relationship.

There's a time for crying and laughing. I listened to God's word in Ecclesiastes and it was talking to me. There were many nights of lying in my bunk man where it became so hard, I couldn't take it and just broke out in tears. I cried for hours. There was nothing I could do to stop those tears. How many have been at that point in life where the pressure is so great, the next option is to give up. Even those who don't know God or His word have broken down in tears from the pressure. This is how we call out to God. When our spirit needs help, it cries. God helps us to release that pressure by opening that valve to tears that lets our spirits free, to let it flow.

In the two years in prison, I had experienced some great times too. There were days that got so bad I had to laugh. Looking back at the guard who yelled so hard I had to cry in frustration, I laugh now because it was all I could do.

Weeping and dancing. What do we weep about? I wept over the fact that I couldn't be home, free. During my first Christmas in jail, I asked my son, "What do you want for Christmas, whatever it is?"

"Daddy, don't worry about it."

"Son what, whatever it is. *Whatever you want for Christmas.*"

My son was 6 years old and he knew what he wanted wasn't appropriate. But I pressured him. I wept because I couldn't be there for him. I had a gang of money, and I thought my money could buy whatever it is that he wanted.

"Daddy, I want you to come home."

My heart sunk and I felt a pain in my gut. My whole soul just lifted hearing those innocent, unselfish words. He didn't ask for a bike or a remote control car a video game. With all the money I had, he wanted his dad home. That was a gut check for me. I wept because all the years I had been out there thinking money was everything, to the children, all they wanted was me.

I spent time with God every night. All I want was His love.

A time for dancing. Dancing is something beautiful and free. You dance to music, a tune, you flow together. It's one on one, you and music. As I thought about dancing I thought about my Father, the Lord. I wanted to be in tune with Him, and dance a glorious dance. You dance for joy because of something that just came upon you. Two years in was a joyous time. I smiled because the next time, I would have four years in on my way home.

Throwing stones. Stones are rocks or pebbles. A stone is thrown with the intention of doing damage, to hurt something or someone, to break something. It is thrown for a purpose. I was throwing stones at my life by wilding out. Every time I did something wrong, used a curse word, I was piercing my soul. A stone, thrown at another person, will always come back. You will only hurt yourself when hurting others.

Embracing. I didn't understand the concept of embracing until I came in here. I had been embracing a life of women, at the strip club thinking, "NIGGA YOU THE MAN!" What is that to embrace? I was just a fool. I was embracing a life of ignorance, crime, foolishness, and lust. It was hard to part with that life. I found a way to break that embrace.

241

Chapter 25

There's a time for finding and losing. God had to bring me to prison in order for me to find myself. God will take you to your lowest point in order to find yourself before you lose your soul.

Readers, reflect on your life, think about these words and dig down deep in your soul to find yourself. Find the child that God made you. Go back to where you took that wrong turn, wherever you got lost. Find yourself before you lose your soul, and your life.

Keeping and giving. Our mothers, fathers, grandmothers, grandfathers, brothers, sisters, friends are here to teach us and give us knowledge. We should think about those gifts and keep them in our hearts. God says, "I place it on every man's heart to know right from wrong." When the things that He places in your heart, when that conviction comes, keep it, hold on to it and do right with it.

We can't hold on to everything. We have to give. I was a dope dealer. I'm in prison charged for conspiracy to distribute six keys of powder cocaine. This is my life. I hope that those out there selling dope, reading this book, will learn something. This is my gift. I am trying to give you knowledge I am trying to give you some understanding. I am giving you a part of me.

God showed me that I wouldn't have had to come to prison if I would have listened. A lot of cats are going to die in prison. In my two years in prison, two people died in there.

Whatever You Want for Christmas

People lost their mothers and fathers, their children, brothers, sisters. I asked God to open my heart and let me be a vessel that He may flow through me to reach His children. This is my gift to you, to save your life, your soul.

A time for tearing. My flesh battled against my spirit all the years in these street. I had to tear myself apart, rip that old man away, pull that flesh off. I had to tear myself apart. Once it's torn, it must be sewn and mended. As I tore the old habits off, I had to find new habits through this word to let God manifest in me. While I tore those old habits, God was sewing new ones. He does this constantly, as long as we allow it.

Thinking about the word love, what comes to mind? What do you think about? What do you love? I didn't know what that word meant until I came to prison. "Luuuuu, luuuu." I couldn't say 'I love you.' I was so lost. The words, "I love you," can be said with meaning. It is a beautiful thing. My girl loved me while I was in the streets, but I didn't know what that meant. For so many nights she cried. She wanted me to do right. How is a man going to do right when he doesn't know what love is. Learn about love means before losing the one who loves you. Whether it's your mother, your father, your brother, your sister, your kids, just stop right now and reflect over your life and see if you have love in your heart. Put pride aside, and commit to loving them.

Chapter 25

I loved my son and all I could think about was what I could buy him when all he wanted was for me to come home. Money is a tool for us to live and survive in this world. It is not love.

A time for love and for hate. The word is a very strong word. The word 'hate' is synonymous to 'destruction'. I hated the man that was in me. I hated what I had become, a child of Satan. He was using me to do whatever he wanted, and I was bringing more and more people to him in the life I was living. I hated that. It was a time for war. What are we at war with? Could it be our parents? Stop, just stop. If you're at war with your parents, stop. If you're at war with your wife, stop. God says, "God, husband, wife, then children." Women, recognize your man, and stop being at war with him. You will lose the battle. You will run that man away and, if you have children, they will be the ones losing. Let God let that man be the man of his house. Get out the trenches with him. Stop fighting him. Let him be a man. Men, be a man that leads. Go to God and ask Him to make you the man that He wants you to be. Without God's word, it is impossible to become a man. God's word is the best role model and guide.

War and peace. When you stop fighting, when you stop being at war, you will find the calm after the storm. After a thunder storm or hail storm, and the wind has died down, and the sun comes out, peace fills the air. With three more years to go in prison, I experienced the most peace I ever had in my

Whatever You Want for Christmas

life, sadly. I let God into my heart. Wherever you are, it can happen. I never understood how people could talk hours about God. But, sitting in prison over the years, I understand now that you can find peace anywhere. Everything has its time and once I understood that, it wasn't hard.

The most difficult part was taking that childish fool, that childish boy, that ignorant boy, and destroying him. I had to come to prison to understand this.

Chapter 26

Locked Up Without Bars

Each night I lay in bed and prayed, thanking God for everything he had done. I would wake up each day, as every other day, back in prison. I rode through '99 looking forward to 2000, the new millennium. "God Lord, I only have two more years left."

New Year's Eve, 2000, we watched the ball drop. Two years left, "Father, Lord, thank you." With two years to the door, the Feds grant a furlough. This was my year for a furlough. Taft now had grass and trees with fruits and vegetables. A bocce court was built along with a basketball court, a football field, baseball field. We were almost at population.

As I tried to leave the past behind me, there were still cats out there wanting to know the business. One cat transferred in, and we were chopping it up. "Kevin, man. You was a fool out there, dawg."

"Yeah, man. But you know that's what it was, it was fun. I had a ball out there."

"I heard about that night when you had that spot over in Norwalk."

"Don't trip. It's in the past."

"Stop acting like you this self holy sanctified ass nigga. Chop it up with your boy. I understand you changed, but a nigga been in here ten years, man. I need to hear something to make me laugh, just some new stories. I hear the same old stories. Just tell me what happened that night"

"It wasn't that serious…

My homeboy pulled up to my spot in Norwalk. He was parked out there, and this esè pulled a gun on him so he called me, 'K, dawg, man. Somebody just pulled a gun on me in front of your house.' I'm like, 'What? Nigga I'll be there in a minute.' So when I pulled up I had my girl and kids in the car with me. I had my Ruger, I was walking down the street screaming, 'Get my kids out of here! Get my kids out of here!' I was screaming, and shit, walking down the middle of the street like I was mothafuckin' Clint Eastwood. While I was screaming and yelling, people were hiding and running. I got my kids up out of there but I had a little change and stuff up in this house that I needed to get but I was over here by myself in they hood. So we went to the spot in Compton,

247

came back to get what I had to get up out of there. We rolled out. When I got to the spot in Compton, I grabbed my K, my 357, I gave one of my homeboys a Beretta 9mm, I gave my other homeboy a 380, one of my other little partners a 357, one of my other little partners a .38. I took my 100 round clip and about 300 rounds of ammo and we went back over there. We were deep.

"We got over there, went in the house, and hit the lights. There I was like some cowboy, telling them to turn off the lights.. wow, whooo. We got over there, opened the garage, pulled in, and hit the lights again. There were about 18-20 esès walking down the street. I told everyone to just be real quiet. They got a little closer and heard clack-clack as I cracked that K and threw the shell in the chamber. The whispered, 'Don't say nothing holmes. Keep walking holmes, keep walking holmes.' That's what I thought. They went to the house across the street trying to be all bad ass and shit. I was trying to provoke some shit, I ain't gone even lie. I was ready to do somebody. But, by the grace of God nothing really happened.

Then my little brother pulled up in his 300Z. An esè walked to the car like he was about to do something. I walked over with the K, cracked it, walk up to him about two feet from his head like 'What, what you gone do?' He put his hand back in his pocket, aww holmes. They were all across the street talking in Spanish. I'm like, 'Nigga, what? I'm in y'all mothafuckin' hood right now, nigga.What? You know what I'm saying, nigga. I'm in y'all hood. This what I'm doing in y'all hood.' They were looking at me like, 'Man who is this cat?' They really don't know who I am they just know I been living over there. So it's kind of crazy, it's crazy man. So that's pretty much what happened that night.

"The next day I went over there, and had a moving truck to come get my stuff because I knew I couldn't stay in their hood anymore."

"Man, you got a little wild."

"Man, it wasn't like I was tripping. I'm not a killer, or a gang banger. But when it comes to my family, I'll die for them. You know you can't really play with me like that, that's a whole 'nother level of me that I don't even understand about myself. It's just a part of me that comes out when its time. So that's kind of what happened with that."

"Yeah, dawg. I just heard you kind of handled your business with them fools. I heard you was just out there, nigga you was on one."

"On one wasn't the word. When you left I went buck wild. I grabbed a couple more plugs you know, things went crazy."

We talked about our wives and our ups and downs, then I went on back to my cube, to read *Our Daily Bread*, then a chapter from the Bible, stayed up in prayer for a minute, then went to sleep.

Chapter 26

Basketball season was coming, so they formed a basketball team. We had A, B, and C league. A was the good league, 6 footers. B league had good players, but everyone was under 6 feet. we had a bomb team that year. A cat won defensive player of the year, everything was cool, and it was fun. We had a track meet that year. I won a race one season. It was all there to pass time, stay in shape, and work out.

In camp, there was no fence. There was a sky diving outfit near the camp, and we could watch them falling, they were free. It was just crazy how the mind would keep itself in prison, locked up, without bars or handcuffs. That invisible fence was no joke. My family kept my mind behind that imaginary fence. My thoughts always drifted to imagining myself going home to my family, my father, my mother, my kids.

I was half way though 2000 and everything was going cool in there. My counselor brought up the furlough. "You could get a furlough now, or wait until February 2001." I gave her a date, February, 14 2001, Valentine's Day. I called my wife up, "Baby, you know, I'm getting my furlough on Valentine's Day." This is when all hell broke loose and things just started going sideways for my marriage. My wife said, "Well, I think I want to be celibate. I don't really think I want to have sex when you come home. I'm not really into that." I knew at that point that she had to be out there sleeping with someone. "You know what, man. Look.

Locked Up Without Bars

If you tripping like that, I ain't really got to come home to you if you ain't feeling me like that."

"I was just thinking about all the things that you did to me in the past that I've overlooked."

"We are in 2001. Why are you going on with that? It's too late to start reminiscing. You're reminiscing over something that doesn't even exist. I thought we were past all of that."

So she continued bringing up all those issues and situations.

"I'm not really trying to feel this. I will be home on Valentines Day. If you don't want me to come home let me know."

This was still 2000, but I was planning for 2001. Over the next six months, I called her and we talked throughout the night, but I could never reach her on the weekends. I stopped calling on weekends.

"I told you I was going to do this time, with you or without you. You're starting to change. Things are starting to change. So I can do this time without you. We don't even have to be together. I'm not even tripping"

We went back and forth. I was talking head to her from jail. Right, hmmm. I stop calling home, everything. She tried calling up there one time to talk to me but I didn't want to talk. I didn't have anything to talk about. It was time for me to start planning to do this time by myself.

Chapter 26

She just popped up there on one visit. She sat looking at me. I told her, "I told you, when I first did this time, that I would do it with you or without you."

"You ain't finna keep yelling at me."

"I'ma keep yelling at you and you gone listen to what I got to say. If not you can get the fuck up and get out of here. I don't give a fuck. If I leave you from here it's going to be the same if I leave you from out there. I'm telling you, you have been changing, and I don't like it. I don't know what the fuck's going on, so if you don't like what I'm saying, bounce. And I'm dead serious. I can go right now. I will turn back the fuck around, go back in there and I'm out of your life. I done seen my kids, I'm cool. You ain't finna keep treating me like this."

She shed a few tears, I shed my tears.

"I'm sorry." and gave me the little rundown. Things smoothed out a little, but that was just the start. Looking back, that was the start of everything going wrong.

Over the few months, we were still taking about the furlough. 2001 come around and I was happy. Another year and I was going home. February 14 was creeping around the corner and we were still having problems about the sex issue. I had been down since '97, so I was going to have sex. I wasn't about to be out there on a furlough with my wife and not have sex. That's crazy.

"Well, we will talk about that when...."

Locked Up Without Bars

"No, we ain't talking about nothing. If you're telling me right now that you ain't feeling me like that, and we ain't having sex, then I'm not coming home. I'm not. I'm not with all that I don't want to have oral sex. I'm not with all that, no. I don't need to come home to this. I will just have my mom or my sister pick me up. I will keep the furlough how it is, you can come with them, they can pick me up and I will roll out, no big deal. Do your thing."

We ironed it out, and she came up there to pick me up. It was Valentines Day 2001. She came along with my two sons, my daughter, my brother in law, and her momma. I'll never forget that. I looked on at the unfamiliar road in the middle of nowhere. All these years at the camp, I didn't know which way was home. It was totally opposite of what I imagined. There was snow along freeway, and I just watched the surroundings. Taft was two and a half to three hours away from Compton. I knew we were close when we passed Magic Mountain. I started feeling happy like a big kid, amazed at the things I hadn't seen in years. We went through Burbank feeling things I couldn't explain. The freeway signs looked familiar, as well as the streets. Burbank, Glendale Boulevard, I saw the Western Avenue exit on the 5. The sign, *5 South coming up*, 110 Harbor. We got on the 110 and started going through Downtown Los Angeles. I got teary eyed thinking I was almost home. The feeling of getting on the 91 was overwhelming, and tears ran down my face. My son looked

up and just stared. He said, "I got a daddy! I got a daddy!"
He was only 7 weeks when I left and this was his first time in
the care with daddy. It was my first time in the car with my
son, and it pierced my heart. "Yes, son. You do have a daddy.
I love you son." That was our first conversation.

When we get off the freeway, we exited at Santa
Fe and by that time I was boo hooing like a baby whimpering
and crying. My wife said, "Stop all that damn crying, man." I
couldn't believe she just said that.

After being in the open for so long, with no poles
or trees, my street looked small. It felt like the streets were
collapsing and closing in on me. Our dorms were open with
15-20 foot ceilings, so when I got to my mom's house, the
chair in the living room look like a little baby doll chair. I
walked in the back, and about 70 of my neighbors were back
there. This is the love I was getting. As I hugged everyone, I
could feel them trembling and just shaking. I saw my
homeboy Craig who I hadn't seen in a while. I saw my
brother –in-law who I hadn't seen in a while, I saw my
neighbor Bert, Monica who I hadn't seen in a while, Tasha,
Tanisha who I hadn't seen in a while, Tutu, Steve, my
homeboy who I did time with and his girl Pump, Blacky, all
these people that I hadn't seen in a while, Fruit, Tyrone,
neighbors. Pee Wee and her kids were there. I was shocked.
Leon and James, my dad's friends… They hugged me, loved
me and I couldn't take it.

Locked Up Without Bars

My mom had a room added on with a couple of stairs. I was shaking and I'm crying. My knees were weak and all I could do was praise, "Father, Lord, thank you Lord, thank you God, Father, Lord, thank you, thank you Lord, thank you Father, Lord, thank you Lord, thank you."

I never understood the term, "I got this monkey on my back." I never understood the foot prints in the sand poem. At that moment I felt as if God dropped me to walk on my own, and all I could do was sit on the step. My sister sat with me hugging and crying. "Thank you Father Lord, thank you, thank you Lord." It was the best feeling of my life. I had never felt this much love and joy in my life. I didn't know what love meant, and I felt it that day.

Blacky had done time so he knew what I was going through. He looked and said, "You alright. You gone be alright. Just take it one day at a time. One day at a time."

I was born again. This was my first time in the real world, born again. I understood the change, I knew it was there, I could feel it, but I couldn't explain it, to be born again in prison and then come home to your family, to your love ones. Anyone who has been in prison knows what I'm talking about. Feel me with this. I was like a baby horse coming out wobbling on his legs. I wobbled all the way up and realized I was on my own two feet. I stretched and felt light. There was no pressure on my back. "Lord thank you."

255

Chapter 26

I shook that off, went down and finish hugging people. I took a picture. My brother-in-law and I embraced each other. After we went through all of this excitement I was anxious to be on my pool table to test out how much tighter I had gotten over the years in prison. I beat my brother-in-law who used to beat me all the time. I had my stick going, my momma made some fried chicken. I hadn't had chicken like momma fried chicken in years. My momma had the best fried chicken that I had ever eaten. I was eating on them chicken wings and sucking on that bone. We were taking pictures, everything is just going and I'm like, "Man."

I have one older brother and a younger brother. My older brother had done time as well. A picture was taken with my momma and the boys now that we were all together since '97. I wasn't even going to come, but I was glad I did. It was just a glorious and beautiful time.

Furlough was only for 12 hours. I was having a great time, and all I could think about after the fun, was having sex. I wanted to make love to my wife. We got ready to leave and I thought we were going to get in my wife's car, but my brother got a limo for us instead. We rode around in the limo, to Torrance to do a little shopping and sightseeing. 12 hours isn't that much time. As we rode around my little girl came and sat on my lap and hugged me. She had a strange look on her face. My wife was next to me. We were together and it was a bitter sweet moment with so many mixed emotions going through the limo. I felt like a star with my daughter on my lap. She was my little princess.

We rode around in the limo all day. My wife had bought a house in Palmdale, so we went out there. My mother-in-law took the kids in the limo and rode around. My wife and I went upstairs. We played around and fondled throughout her visits, she wasn't with having sex in the visiting rooms like most cats did. Some cats made babies while in prison, but I couldn't get down like that. But that night, I did. When I tell you I got down, it was like, "Whooo!" It had been years, so you know we enjoyed ourselves.

The limo took us back to Taft. During the drive, my youngest son Kristopher, who was born just before I started my sentence, sat there staring at me and said, "Daddy, I love you."

"I love you too. man."

Then he laid his head on me.

We arrived at Taft, and I walked out of the limo like a new man. I felt good. I had a bounce in my step. Everyone assumed I paid for the limo, and that I was still ballin'. I got back to my dorm. My bunkee was in there, and we chopped it up, while I relived my day through my stories

Chapter 27

Nigga, Nigga, Nigga, Nigga

It was playoff day for our basketball team, and I was in the basketball game looking like a jumping bean, all over the place. I had so much energy the dudes on the yard were amazed. I was everywhere. "If that's what furloughs do to you, we all need ONE." and I laughed 'cause my load was definitely lighter. They knew I got some loving. They called it getting your nuts out the sand- that meant they were heavy from too much sperm so they dragged. That was the saying so I ain't got that on my back.

2001 was the year all the weight was lifted. I had one more furlough before the end of my sentence. So nothing was going to bother me. I was on the yard doing my time, having fun, chilling.

Niggas, Niggas, Niggas, Niggas

They opened a computer program for Word and Excel. I enrolled and get that up under my belt. I was doing my best to stay busy. My last year seemed worse than my first year, despite the lifted weight. It was rough to be back in here as a caged bird after feeling a hint of freedom. I felt like the cats in there didn't even know what they were missing. I knew that once I got out of there, I would do my best never to come back.

We got some new cats on the yard with this FCI tough guy mentality. They had a different kind of attitude. I got into it with one of them. He was taking a gang of mess, "Nigga, nigga, nigga, nigga, nigga, nigga." all in my face.

"What I do to you homeboy? I haven't called you 'nigga.' I haven't called you out of your name."

"Nigga, I'll fuck you up."

It didn't really affect me since I was close to going home.

"That's cool. Just get off the court."

Now one of my other homeboys, whispered, "Man, look. Dude ain't no punk. He might look like that, but he ain't no punk. So the best thing to do is kind of just let that one go." And he just stopped. This homeboy used to get work from me so he knew what I was about. He didn't show up during a drought after making an order, so I told him that next time he wanted to get some work from me, he had to pay an extra $2,000 for each one. If not, then bounce.

Chapter 27

As I walked back to the dorm by his cube, he said, "Man, Kevin. Wassup? I need to talk to you. I want to apologize for the way I acted today. That was totally out of my character."

I mean this is how things were going through 2001. I took a few courses, met a few people, asking people if they knew anyone who was hiring on the streets. I didn't want to have to go through the whole looking in the paper going on dead runs. I needed a job, and was trying to find as many connections as I possibly could. I didn't want to get into anymore trouble. I didn't want to get into any fights so I kept to myself this last year.

One of my homeboys came in that had been down 12, 13 years and he ended up being my bunkee. He had about 12 more to go. One of my other partners, through my brother-in-law came up there with 9 in and some more to go. We laughed at them because cats that come from the FCI were kind of crazy. They went into the room, counted the mop heads, broom handles, and all the equipment in there. One cat was walking around with a shank up his sleeve and a jacket on, in 100 degree weather. We told them it wasn't the FCI or the pen, so kick back. It took them a while to adjust. But there were some tough guys that came in. I was by myself in the dorm, when a new cat arrived. I had the bottom bunk This new cat said, "I'm getting that bottom bunk," as soon as he touched the yard. I heard about it all the way from Unicore. I was gritting all day hearing that he wanted to whoop my ass

260

and take my bottom bunk. He was supposed to be some tough cat from the FCI.

"Looks like it's on," they were whispering. When I got to my bunk, he said, "Wassup, man. I want that bottom bunk."

"Check this out partner. I don't make the bed arrangements, so if you got a problem with having the bottom bunk, I think you need to go talk to the counselor or the case manager. That's who probably can help you out."

"I'm just saying, dawg. I want this bottom bunk."

"I ain't gone discuss it with you 'cause, like I said, if you got a problem with this bottom bunk, you want it, you can go talk to the counselor or case manager."

"Look, I want the bottom bunk."

I didn't say nothing else. I finished taking off my jacket and got situated.

"Man, I want the bottom bunk."

I didn't say anything to him any more. I just watched him, letting him know I was watching him. He was about 2-3 inches taller than me, and probably had me by about 20 pounds. For me, that ain't nothing. For the next few weeks it was crazy because every time he moved, I was up tweaking. It seemed stupid that I was on my way home and I had to deal with this. Everyday for almost four months it was, "Whassup, man. How you doing? Whassup, man? How you doing?" He finally responded, "Whassup, man. How you doing?"

"I'm cool."

We talked and he finally admitted to coming at me wrong at the beginning. "Don't trip. It is what it is. That's just prison." This is how they get down up in there. When you learn how to respect a man, you can easily break through the tough guy. That was the last incident in there since I was trying to stay cool with 2002 right around the corner. If I fought or did anything wrong or crazy, I pretty much could lose all my rights. I already had my boss up in Unicore telling me that if it were up to him, I would not get another furlough. He was just a hater for no reason. I wasn't worried about what he had to talk about. Cats and Federal Guards would talk head, jock us and bother us.

I got my second furlough in December 2001. I left on the 24th. I was able to get Christmas and a few days after Christmas at home. My wife came to pick me up on the 24th and everything was going cool. We rode around before getting home in Palmdale. My brother-in-law brought me some clothes. I put on the gear thinking I was fly and smilin'.. We went to dinner at Tony's on the pier in Redondo Beach, and enjoyed each other's company. She and I went to the toy shop and she asked me everything that was going on in the camp. We had a deep conversation about other women, the money, the strip clubs. I told her, "I married you. I haven't even thought about none of that stuff."

"Kevin, you only married me right before you went to jail."

"True, but it doesn't change the fact of the man that I've become, that I do love you."

No matter what I said, she was still trippin'. I told her all about my past, about threesomes, strip clubs, how I was out there wilding out. I was opening all the doors, hoping it would bring us closer.

Back in 2000 when she and I were going through problems in prison, I had another friend who came to visit me. My wife came to visit the week after my friend came by, and I told her about it out of respect.

Back to 2001- She was re-playing all this in her head, and she couldn't take it. Most men would have kept the other visit a secret from their wives. Most people might think I'm real bold or crazy, or she's real stupid. In my perspective, if I'm going to be with you or you with me, I'm going to be honest.

During the five day furlough, we did a whole lot of talking. She was feeling insecure, thinking I married her as a last resort because I was going to jail. She was by far the last resort. I had a choice of other women to marry but I chose the mother of my kids. I was going to make it work.

Chapter 27

"I think we can make it through this. You just did almost five years with me. We made it through prison. Everything should be cool."

She wasn't trying to hear that so, the night passed by in silence. I made the best out of the next couple of days despite the drama.

Back to prison and 2002, my year, was one day away. I never thought I was going to see 2002. "Thank you Lord!" It was a Happy New Year. I was on my knees crying, "Father, Lord, thank You!" All of those going out in 2002 partied. Other cats partied year after year, and this was our year. We were going home this year. If I get six months in the half way house, I'd be leaving in April. I didn't know what kind of half way house I would get. Over the next few months, we rode it out. Now my crimey, D, was going home before me. A crimey is a person you catch your case with. He was heading out in March. Somewhere in March, he asked me for my information.

"Man, you know where my mom and dad live."

"Aww,man. You ain't giving me your information?"

"Man. I'm not messing with you. I'm in here right now because of you. Why am I going to give you my information to hook up? Not happening. I mean, if you need to holler at me, just go slide by moms and pops house."

The next day, I had a team meeting with my counselor, case manager, and the rest of the people over my case. Since

Niggas, Niggas, Niggas, Niggas

I had never been in trouble, they granted me the six months in a halfway house. The leave date was April 15th. I quit Unicore, and started winding down. I passed out clothes, books, all the things I didn't want to take with me. I gave all my nice sweats, shirts, and jackets to all the cats that had maybe 5, 10 more years left. I gave away clippers, radios, brushes, combs, shoes. I wanted to share my books, hoping it would help them better themselves the way it helped me. That last month was long. Without work or books, there was really nothing to do besides watch the clock. I wrote a letter to one of my friend's relatives about getting me a job. I contacted everybody I could so I could start work immediately.

April 15th came, and I the option of catching the bus or getting a ride. I took the bus pass, and transferred to the half way house.

I went to prison on August 2nd 1997, a Friday. I left prison on April 15th 2002, a Monday. As I flashed back over the five years it just seemed like a really long weekend. I was finally free!

Chapter 28

I'm Home Now

I was on my way to the halfway house. The halfway house was meant as a transition to get an inmate from prison to freedom. When I arrived, I checked in. There were requirements while in there. I had to get a job, and give them 25% of the paycheck. I was able to leave during the day to work, but I had to return before a certain time. It wasn't total freedom, but after 4 years or more in prison, most people felt free.

The halfway house was co-ed, with girls on one side and men on another. Some of the cats had been down so long they were horny, so it went down in there. When they closed the doors at night, there were cats going over there, girls coming over here. I just wanted to get out of there.

I'm Home Now

I was placed in a room with a couple of Iranians. I had to deal with some racism. They always tried turning the lights out when I was trying to read. We went back and forth about different issues.

Each day, I would go out looking for a job. It wasn't as easy as it was supposed to be. I couldn't get my license when I realized I owed back child support. My sister had to drive me around go take care of that.

I was suppose to have an interview with one of my friend's people, but that didn't go through. The half way house was on my back about getting a job. If I didn't get a job, they threatened to send me back to prison. I was almost at the point where I was ready to go back, as frustrated as I was. My wife and I were having problems. Now that I was free, she seemed like a totally different person. Was it everything that I revealed to her during my furlough? Maybe she thought that now that I was home, things would change. I felt like going back to prison to finish this time out.

In jail, I missed a lot of things, and especially things we usually take for granted. I missed my family and those close to me, but I also missed things like taking a bath, walking on carpet, being able to eat what I wanted to eat any time of the night. It was painful living off of memories. They took everything away from me physically and gave me a thought to live on.

Chapter 28

Without money and family support, life was hard. There was a lot of pressure on me to make things right.

There were cats out here that still owed me a lot of money. My brother-in-law said he was going to arrange a vehicle, and that didn't pan out. Other cats were supposed to slide me some money. I was out here stuck. My wife let the house go into foreclosure, her car note was due, the light bill needed to be paid, water bill, gas bill, phone bill. I came home and this stuff was slapping me in the face. I was in a half way house and I couldn't move. I couldn't take this pressure.

I got a job with my cousin who has a day care in Palmdale. The halfway house was in El Monte at least an hour away. I got my license and my sister let me use her car. I had to deal with this until I got out of the halfway house so I could move around?

I was already irritated and I came in one day, after being out trying to get a job, and my roommate had set all my stuff outside. I never touch another man's stuff with out asking, so I got real hot and went into the room. They were both talking a gang of shit, "We will whoop yo' ass."

"Okay, right." So I slid up out the door to go grab a few of my homeboys and asked them to make sure the people that run the half way house weren't coming. I was going to do something to this dude running his mouth real fly. When I went back in there, they saw all my homeboys out side. I told the one dude, that really wasn't wolfing, he was just co-signing. I said, "Man, look. Get yo' shit and get up out of here. I'm about to whoop yo homeboy ass. Fuck that."

"Oh no, no, no it's not like that."

"Get yo' mothafuckin' ass up out of here." My homeboys snatched him out of the room. Them mothafuckas started screaming. I was in the room, the other cat was fucking hiding and shit. I was damn near about to crack him and my homeboys warned me, "Kevin, Kevin the people coming." So we squashed it. The guards came by after hearing the commotion and I explained, "Look, I keep telling these fools to stop touching my stuff. They keep touching it, keep being disrespectful." I mean, that was what it was. I was already irritated, shit wasn't going right for me, and I was tired of them being disrespectful. I had dealt with that enough, so I was cool.

The dude that was running the half way house decided to separate us. They put me in a room with some brothers. I didn't want to share a room with them either. They were in there blowing, getting drunk, with cell phones. I didn't want to get caught up with this, but I didn't have that much longer.

Once I secured a job, I had to pay the halfway house 25% of my paycheck per the requirements. I was released to go home on confinement. After almost 5 years of being gone, I found that my wife had her way of doing things. She was working, the kids were in school but not doing homework.

Chapter 28

They were wilding out. I felt like I came home to a zoo. I looked at all the bills pilled up wondering how I was going to manage it. I figured since I used to own the restaurant, which has since closed, I would try to get into catering. I would build my clientele once I got out of this half way house. In the meantime, I had to keep my job at the daycare.

From the halfway house, I caught the bus to my job. I couldn't believe that after thirty-one years of life I was on the bus. I actually never rode the bus in my life until then. I went from making anywhere from $10,000.00 to $50,000.00 dollars a week sometime more, and came home to this. There were cats out there that owed me a couple hundred thousand. These were people I helped, people I put down, people I turned my plug over to.

All this was going through my head while riding the bus. I didn't tell on anyone, didn't snitch, I did my time as a man, so I thought my connect this time would be even stronger. They knew I was home because they were all calling my momma's house. These people aren't giving me my money, they're not trying to help me. My brother-in-law didn't take care of me by giving me the truck. Between the bus, the bills piled up, the people on my back at the halfway house and my house going into foreclosure, my head was spinning. All I could think of was, "Damn, my people calling me, man. I could go pick up this sack real quick, hit a lick for about $100,000.00 in about a month. Just one lick and I could take care of all of this." I was sitting there actually planning it in my head until I looked over my shoulder and noticed MDC. That was a memory, right there, letting me know I shouldn't do it. I was free, and I was going to ride this bus.

It ended up not being so bad. I met a few older ladies catching the same route. I made friends on the bus. I started looking at it as a whole new way of life that I didn't know about before. So I embraced it, and was thankful that I was there. I was thankful to be free.

The battle was hard. They say that money isn't everything, but when money consumes 90% of your day in life, it begins to be everything. I kept thinking about how I could make more money. I was going back and forth to work praying, "Lord, let me keep my house. Don't let them turn off the lights. Don't let them turn off the water." I was calling everybody I knew, everybody. I was getting in touch with cats asking for $500.00 or $100.00. I had my dignity but I lost all my pride. I was taking money from people I never did business with before and paying the bills. These people came through. My prayer was, "Father, Lord. In the name of Jesus, let some people open their hearts so that you can work through them." I prayed it every day. I asked the Lord to provide away to keep the 6 bedroom house that was more than I needed.

I started my catering and was blessed with my first call. It was a catering job for 400 people. I didn't have the money

Chapter 28

or the equipment, but I took the job. One thing I did learn in these streets was how to hustle. I never turned down any money. I was given the deposit for the job, but couldn't cash it since I didn't have enough money in the bank. It would take four days to clear, so I asked brother-in-law for a loan to get all the things that I needed. He loaned the money. I rented the equipment and set up a kitchen outside near my BBQ pits to do the job. I had to report my every movement to the halfway house, or it would be a problem. As they were trying to get in touch with me during the job, I ignored the calls. I knew if I didn't, they would take 25%. I wanted to keep all of this. I knocked out the job, paid my brother-in-law back and got my money. It was a nice amount, but not enough to cover all the bills. I needed to hold on to my house and save my family.

I finally left the halfway house permanently in October of that year. I still had to deal with my probation officer, with scheduled meetings and drug testing eight days a month, or twice a week. It was random so I had to make sure I was at home at certain times to take the call. Each inmate has a number, so if my number came up, I had to report in to take the drug test.

One of my homeboys bought a '92, Saturn for me to get back and forth. I had to be at work at 7:30 from Palmdale. The drug testing place opened at 5:30am, and if I wasn't on the road by 6am, I'd be late. So I was there right when the

I'm Home Now

doors opened, first one, in and out. It was an ongoing thing to have the officer pop up at my house at any time.

Once a prison sentence is done, the rules continue, so I was free, but still a prisoner. A week after I got out the halfway house, my wife received a letter from a law firm, saying we had to come up with $9,000.00 in six days or they would foreclose on the house. When I left, she had enough money that, if she would have used it right, everything would have been fine. She used some of the money for the down payment on the house. The house note was twelve hundred and went up to fourteen hundred since she got behind. She had to have been behind at least 6 months for the foreclosure fees to be $9,000.00. I didn't understand what she had been doing out there. That was the subject of our first really big argument. She said she had been trying to survive.

"You ain't been trying to survive! You been out here flossin'! This is what I was trying to warn you about when I was gone, when the kids were coming to visit me every week in new clothes, and you driving a new car. I get home, now show me one bill that ain't in the red. Light bill in the red 'bout to be turned off. Gas bill in the red, 'bout to be turned off. Water bill in the red 'bout to be turned off. Now I got a note saying that I have to come up with nine thousand dollars in almost six days? Come on, man! A forty-five hundred dollar tummy tuck? Was it really worth it? I get home my kids got bad grades. I don't know what you've been doing

Chapter 28

but you haven't been doing what you were suppose to be doing. This is why, when I call home while I was gone, you weren't answering the phone? This is why we going through everything that were going through."

I was smashing because, at this point, I didn't want to come home to this. The only reason I kept coming back were the kids.

I went to my room and got on my knees, "Father, Lord. I don't know how I'm going to do this, but I need nine thousand dollars." I was on the phone calling everybody. One of my cats that I did time with slid a $1000 to me, another one of my old homeboys slid me $2000. I got $1000 from the catering job and a loan for $2500 from my job. $6500. I still had $2500 to come up with. I ask pops, he didn't do it. I asked my brother-in-law and he said no. I just kept praying. I called one of my other homeboys who gave me $2000 which put me at $8500. $500 more. I had some jewelry from the past, so I went to my jeweler and showed him a piece I bought for $3000. After spending at least $50,000 through him over the years, and referring others who spent hundreds of thousands there, I thought for sure he'd give me a good deal. "Look, I don't need this. What can you give me for this? I only need $500. Can you give me that?" This fool told me he would give me $250. I took it because I needed it, but I was hot! All these people were doing me wrong. People that I helped put food on the table. I was hurt. I would have died

I'm Home Now

for some of them. I would have put my life on the line for these people.

I still had to come up with $250 more dollars by the next day. I made calls, calls, calls. One of my cousins gave me $100. I came up with the rest, and took it all down there to the bank in a cashier's check.

They say pride come before destruction. Never have too much pride to ask, because it could ruin you. God works in his way, not our way. Over the years I had been in the word strong. God showed me how loyal He was to me. I was tested with my people coming to meet me. I could've hopped in the game and sold dope but I didn't do that. I hopped on the bus, instead. I was thirty-one and I started my life over. I knew there were people who owed me. I could get out there and play cowboy, but what would that do besides put me back in jail. I didn't want to do another minute in jail. I spent time in prayer. That's what I learned all of the past years. I saved our house and by the grace of God, came up with $9,000.00 in six days.

Chapter 29

$8.00-An-Hour-Ass-Nigga

I turned thirty-two, on September 22, 2002 I celebrated my freedom from the halfway house. I was home and making $8.00 an hour. But I was free. My wife's car's crank shaft broke because she never put oil in it. So, now we only had the Saturn. No car, so she decided to stop working.

"Kevin, I'm tired and I don't want to work. I'm just tired and I need a break."

"Okay. If that's what you're going to do, I can't make you do otherwise. No big deal."

In the meantime, I was getting my grind on, hustling up catering jobs here and there, doing what I had to do to make it. I was making it.

One morning, Deborah and I got into an argument on the phone while I was at work. At the time, while I was out of prison and the halfway house, I was still on home confinement for six months. I would be out by April. During home confinement, I had to continue to call the officer to let them know my every move. "Hey, I'm leaving. I'm going to the store. Hey, I'm back." I was still a prisoner and couldn't move around the way I needed to.

"Kevin, how we going to make it?"

"Your life hasn't changed. You got a tummy tuck that cost $4500, a new car, the clothes. Your life ain't changed." It was the same argument about money, and her being gone every weekend somewhere I couldn't reach her.

"I'm home. I'm about to build this life back. Hopefully you can come with me. If not, I'm going to make a way and I'm going to be alright."

She continued, "Kevin, how we going make it? What we going to do? How we gone make it? You ain't nothing but an *eight dollar an hour ass nigga.*"

Whoa! Talk about a low blow. This was from a woman, who hadn't worked, who had been well kept, with a little punk-ass degree from Devry. This was coming from a woman who I took care of and sacrificed my life for.

"I just want you to remember one thing, for the rest of your life. That I'm an eight-dollars-an-hour-ass-nigga. Remember that!"

"I didn't mean it like that."

Chapter 29

"Yes, you did. And I'm going to hang up." Before she could say anything else, I hung up the phone.

"This bitch just called me an eight-dollars-an-hour-ass-nigga!"

Instead of thinking, "This man just saved this house. He got the lights, gas, water bill caught up. Nothing is in the red. He's handled his business." She's calling me an *eight-dollars- an-hour-ass-nigga* because she can't splurge like she used to. She came home with a cell phone, and I took it.

"You don't need this."

She was renting a TV. I took it back. Anything she didn't need, I took it. She was basically saying that I was trying to control her life. She was out there flossing like she was some fly-ass bitch, letting everything get out of control. If I didn't come home and control things, it would have fallen completely apart. Instead of listening and trying to follow me and understand what type of man I was, she wanted to challenge me. She was hanging out with her independent home girls. All of them were independent. I got respect for independent women, but if you a kept woman, don't try and act like an independent woman, when you haven't done nothing besides fuck off someone else's money. She developed an attitude over that past 4 or 5 years, living off of my money, working, doing whatever the fuck she wanted to do.

$8.00-An-Hour-Ass-Nigga

That 'eight-dollars-an-hour-ass-nigga' was just a low blow. I had a bad day at work feeling fucked up. As soon as I got home I said, "Your eight-dollars-an-hour-ass-nigga is home! And, let me tell you something.." I had been trying not to curse. I had been trying to be cool. My sister and everybody else were calling me Gandhi. I was in my word, trying to live right, "...hold up. You got me fucked up. I don't know what type of mothafucka you think I am. You couldn't have sold your mothafuckin' pussy and came up with $9000 in six days. And you fucking with me like this, cause I'm trying to tell you to kick back. Life is going to be alright for us.

Let me get out the half way house and this home confinement bullshit. Let me be able to move around, get to some of my money, do what I need to do. We will be alright. Quit tripping.

Your stupid, mothafuckin', ass can't understand that. All you worrying about is me trying to control you. I don't give a fuck what you do. Have I ever asked you once, since I been home, who you've been with? I asked you, 'was you faithful,' cause that's what you said, and I ain't asked you shit else, nothing. But you want to fuck with me and call me an eight-dollars-an-hour-ass-nigga because I'm trying to make a future for us. Fuck you."

Valentines day 2003 approached and she started talking about this Lexus. We were looking at cars. Things had been

279

Chapter 29

kind of cool for a minute. I was making some decent money with the catering business. We were out of debt, were not in the red, things looked up for us.

My credit was cool, besides some things she fucked off so I bought the Lexus, brand new '03 Lexus. In front of the finance guy I said, "Damn an eight-dollars-an-hour-ass-nigga ain't doing to bad, huh," and just started laughing. "You're going to remember you called me that for the rest of your life." She thought it was funny, but I wasn't joking.

Home confinement ended that April, and the marriage was rough. She has a crazy attitude about wanting to run the street with her friends and 'do what she do'. In the back of my mind I thought, "Either you're trying to push me away every time things start going cool, or you got a cat that you've been fucking with over the years and don't know how to tell me." So I asked her, "Are you trying to push me away? Or you just don't want this?" Her reason was thinking about all the things that I did to her in the past and how stupid she was. She was feeling dumb for waiting on me. "That's crazy. What you're going through now you should have gone through while I was gone. You wait 'til I come home to get everything in order and in line to start tripping like this. It doesn't make sense to me. I mean, we made it through the bullshit. We're suppose to be living right now, happy with each other."

$8.00-An-Hour-Ass-Nigga

My daughter received her report card with F's and D's. My wife wanted me to go curse her out and whoop her. She sent her upstairs to her room. I went upstairs and saw her crying, "Daddy, I try hard but I just can't get it." I looked at her and I saw the pain in her eyes. "Baby, look. Don't worry about it. You're not dumb, or stupid. You know your daddy has been gone. It's my and your mothers fault that you're like this. Show me what's wrong."

"I don't understand math."

She showed me her math. I helped her with her math. She still didn't understand so I planned to enroll her in Kumon learning center, the next day. I went back downstairs and asked my wife, "What kind of woman are you? You want me to whoop our daughter's ass? She's having trouble because of you. You haven't taught her nothing. You been so busy these last 3 years trying to be fly, trying to be a cute ass broad, and you haven't spent any time with these kids. You haven't spent no time in the house. All you've been doing is out here wilding out in these streets. If you would have spent that $4,500.00 on her education instead of a tummy tuck, she would not be like this." And there she went, "Fuck you. You don't know were I've been. I've been trying to keep this house up while your mothafuckin' ass was gone."

"Keep what up? Show me what you've been keeping up besides yourself. What you been keeping up ain't that mothafuckin' great, so I don't know what you've been out

281

here doing. I know ain't shit been kept right with this family. My daughter ain't doing right in school. But don't worry about it. We going to fix that."

Over the next 6, 7 weeks in Kumon, her grades went straight up. She caught on. "Daddy, I'm not dumb, huh? I'm smart!"

"Yeah, baby. You're smart. I told you that."

My wife and I were having problems. I was trying to figure, through the word, if I should stay in that marriage. In Matthew it mentions divorce. It points out that divorce isn't the answer, but spouses had to be equally yoked. I went into prison one way, and came home a total different person. I was a boy when I left and she was a girl. I came home a man and she was still a girl. we were two different people. I looked at her thinking how foolish I was. Was this what I was? It had been years since we last lived together, so I really don't know how or who she is. But now I was forced to see this, and I was seeing it through the eyes of a man. I was seeing it through the eyes of someone who had matured. I was torn between two worlds.

I got on my knees to pray. Do I stay? Do I go? I was trying. It became so hard for me that one night, I broke down in tears. My baby girl came down stairs and asked, "Daddy, what's wrong?"

"I can't take it, momma."

"I don't want you to go, daddy."

$8.00-An-Hour-Ass-Nigga

"Momma, what? What do yo want me to do? You want me to stay here and be miserable and suffer?"

"Yeah."

That was another low blow in my gut. I knew my kids needed me. She had come so far with her grades, and her momma wasn't spending any time with them.

I went back and fourth to work. My kids asked what their mom did for work. "You go to work. You take care of us. Mommy don't cook. She don't clean up. She don't do nothing."

I went back and forth, spending so much time in Matthew reading about divorce and marriage. I was stuck. The bible tells us that if adultery has not been committed there is no reason for divorce. The bible wasn't showing me a way out besides being unequally yoked. I asked God what to do. I caught her in lie after lie. She would say, "I'm going to do what I want, whenever, and go were I want when I get ready to."

"You're right. I just won't be apart of it."

The next day she went out with her home girls to a day spa or whatever. When she came back I was gone. I kept telling my sister that when I had enough money to get out of there, I was out. I had enough money to leave and be able to help her with my kids.. A man is going to be a man and I couldn't keep allowing her to disrespect me.

Chapter 29

The day I left, I went to get a hair cut. I was at the barbershop talking to one of my homeboys telling them what's going on. I vented because I was in so much pain. She had a friend in there who thought I was clowning. I was torn between staying and leaving. I stayed for the kids' sake. I left for my own. I walked out on my kids, and that's why I was in pain. I sacrificed for my family but we couldn't work together, or see eye to eye. I couldn't understand how, this woman who came to visit me every week for four years could be trippin' like this. I walked away from my family.

A year after being off of home confinement I walked out of the house. I moved into an empty apartment at the complex my sister owned. Over the next few weeks, I hired a paralegal to handle my divorce. I didn't want to prolong the marriage. It was painful, as much as I hate to say it. I could barely walk some days. I was in so much pain for walking out of there. My stomach was in knots, my legs were wobbly. I just walked away from my family. I didn't see my kids and after been away from them for almost five years, that was a painful time.

I did eventually meet a female. Her name was Shae. We hung out and things were cool. She was a female from my past. We went to the movies, kicked it. I still called my wife every day, trying to talk her into getting back together for the sake of the family. I was trying to get here to see my side. I had been tying to build a family. I explained that I wasn't

284

trying to control her. As our conversations went on, I asked her if she was sure that she wanted to do this. I didn't understand why she wanted to hang out. She responded, "I didn't call you. You walked. That's a decision you made. So deal with it," then hung up.

My days went by. One night, after having fun at a movie and dinner, I went back to Shae's place. It felt strange. I hadn't tried to sleep with her, since I was married.

I hadn't cheated on my wife since we were married. I didn't even desire another woman. When I looked at women I didn't see them as a piece of meat or as flesh as I once did. God has opened my eyes to a whole new way of life. When I said I loved my wife and I loved my family, I truly meant that.

Being on this date was more or less a passing of time. Something to free my mind from my thoughts. Until that night, there had been no hugging or kissing. I was feeling myself, she was feeling her self we kissed, we played around. The feeling is good because my sex life hadn't been too great.

My marriage had no intimacy at all, no connection outside of my furlough. I was still in the mind set of being married, still trying to be right. In my mind I knew she wasn't my wife. I left, I started the divorce process, but I was still married. I felt guilty. I was bugging out. I went from a player, wilding out in the streets, to a man feeling guilty because I was kissing another woman. I had really grown in my walk with God.

I backed up, and we just kind of kicked it for the rest of the night. Over the next few weeks, I was still calling my wife everyday, sending her emails, trying to make it work, and trying to move on at the same time.

One night, I thought talking to her in person would have a greater impact, and possibly cause her to change her mind. So I left LA and drove to Palmdale. She insisted, "I'm not trying to talk to you. I don't have nothing to say to you." She was being real cocky.

"Wow okay. I got you." I didn't want to be the typical black man, come home, leave his family, separate, let my kids grow up in a home without a father. But at that point there was no hope.

I left Palmdale and hooked up with my little friend. We hung out, went to grab something to eat, and went back to my place. We were kissing and messing around again but this time, we took off our clothes and touched each other. It was feeling real good and I was smiling, but feeling really nervous. I'm telling you, man. I was nervous. I felt like a little kid, laying there shaking, and trembling.

"What's wrong?" She asked.

"Do you know I have not been with another women outside of my wife since '97. That was six years ago. I'm nervous."

$8.00-An-Hour-Ass-Nigga

"Don't worry. It's alright."

"No, you don't understand." Now mind you back in the day this is somebody I done flipped all kinds of ways. I mean we done ripped sheets up, freaking so hard. She was really tripping off of me. "Kevin, you know. You're alright."

She was ready. I slid up under the sheets and pulled them up over me. I balled up under the sheets sitting there, picturing myself in my head thinking, "Man, you a fool." She laughed at me. I thought, "I'm new to this. I'm not this freak anymore." I didn't know how to respond, so she pulled the sheets down. It was like riding a bike from that point. The freak came out and we went at it. When we finished I laid there and I could feel that old Kevin coming back.

Once I slept with this woman who wasn't my wife, I opened the door to spirits of lust. Those spirits started coming in and I could feel my personality start to change. I felt good, and it was just the inspiration I needed to stop calling my wife to bug her. My days went back to hanging out with Shae, having fun, getting up, going to work and hanging out with her again

Chapter 30

Don't Play With Me

September 2003. I told my wife not to hold the kids against me in the event of a divorce, so I was getting them every weekend. Shae and I hung out through the summer and by this time, she was becoming attached. Every week, "Kevin, won't you stay over?" I was cool and went home every day. I was going to work trying to get my business going off the grown. Things felt like they were going in a positive direction. I couldn't get back with my wife since she was on another planet.

Don't Play With Me

Shae and I were hanging tough, but my feelings for her didn't go beyond friendship. She insisted on more, but I had to keep my distance. She kept on asking me to spend the night. "Look come on, Shae. You, me, and the sun we will never wake up together so just kick back."

That old me was starting to surface again. I was trying to fight it but once I opened that floodgate to those spirits, they rush on in. The bible speaks of a man, who, once he returns to his old ways, is like a dog returning to vomit. Once those spirits leave you the first time, they come back with a vengeance. They bring stronger spirits to attack you. All kind of doors started to open.

I thought about what I just said to her. They were some of the worst words that ever came out of my mouth, but I couldn't take it back. I thought about how well everything was going, from work, to my business and the children, and I wondered, "God, why couldn't my marriage work? What did I do? Where did I go wrong?" I couldn't think of any thing. Whoever this other cat was, that possibly came in between us, had her nose wide open or something.

One Saturday, on my way home, I saw a cute little woman next to me on the freeway while I was driving. She smiled so I waved at her, and she waved back. "Hi, how you doing?" I don't have a problem meeting a girl anywhere. She rolled her window down and I repeated, "Hi, how you doing?" We were yelling through the noise on the freeway. "Hi!"

"What's your name?"

She told me her name, I told her mine. I held up my cell phone, "You got a phone?"

"Yeah."

"What's your number?"

She yelled it out to me. I punched it in my phone, and I dialed it right there. "Hi, so where you coming from?"

"I'm just coming from picking up my daughter."

"I been out just kind of chilling today, went shopping, went and got me a facial, manicure, pedicure."

"Yeah, that's right. Where do you go to get your facial, hands, and feet done?"

"It's this place in Cerritos."

"Well it's this place in Torrance that's kind of cool."

"You're going to have to take me there one day. So what are you doing later on?"

"I have to drop my daughter off and run some errands."

"okay, cool. Hit me later on when you're done."

My day went by and I stopped by my sister's house, mom's and pop's house, chilling, just having a little fun. Later on that night, I was laying on my sister's couch. I hadn't gotten my own place yet. I guess in the back of my mind, I kept hoping that maybe my wife and I could possibly work it out. I could see the looks on there faces when they saw other families. I knew if I got a new place for myself, that would be final.

I got a phone call around 11 o'clock at night from the girl on the freeway. I told her about my past, prison, the divorce and let her know she sounded real cool. Somehow we got on the conversation of sex. She said, "Well I haven't had none in a while, and I'm kind of horny tonight. You kind of cute."

"Girl, you better stop playing with me."

"No, serious."

"You saying I'm cute to say what?"

"I mean, if you was over here something could possibly happen."

"Okay, you don't live that far. So if you ain't serious, don't play with me."

"I'm dead serious. But if you come over here you better come ready to have fun cause I don't think you could handle this."

Now the spirits were in me and they were coming out little by little. Back in the day, you know how I was meeting the girls. I done changed my life, but I opened that gate to all those spirits.

"I'm on my way over there. Give me the address."

I got over there, I wasn't in the house ten minutes before we went at it, like two monkeys. We were flipping each other, going crazy for a good two hours. By the time we finished she was like, "Whooo, man. I haven't had no sex like that in a long time."

She wasn't lying. I hadn't came that many times in a long time. I was sitting on her couch thinking, "Man, this is great! Man, it was nice."

I heard someone scrambling in the other room and it was her daughter waking up.

"I'm going to go head and get out of here." 'Cause I wasn't spending the night with a woman that wasn't mine.

On my way home I felt Satan was trying to come at me sending drugs and all these people my way. I didn't bite. So he figured, "I'll attack him with his marriage, 'cause I already got that." I prayed, "Lord, you done took everything from me. There's nothing else for you to take." Through the word, the good spirits were talking, "Be careful, son. He's trying to tempt you. He's trying to tempt you with drugs, 'cause it's not about money for you. He took your wife, and now he's coming after you by sending women your way." I wasn't the best looking man in the world, and although handsome, not to the point where a girl I meet will drop her drawls on the day I meet her. *"Satan, you funny man. You are going to give me all my desires, huh. But unfortunately, I don't desire sex. I just desire companionship right now."* And that was what he was bringing me through these women. "Father, Lord. Don't let me slip back out here. I don't want this. I want to be married. Don't let me slip back out here.

Don't Play With Me

Help me please. I done been with two different women already and I'm not even divorced. Come on, Lord. I need your strength Father Lord, help me."

The next morning I got a phone call from my wife. "Hello? It's me." and I jumped up, "Hey!" you know I was happy.

"What are you doing today?"

"I really don't have any plans."

"Why don't you hang out with me and the kids today?"

"Where are you guys going?"

"We're going to Dave and Busters"

"Okay, cool! So where are you guys at?"

"We're at home."

"Okay, no problem."

I got dressed, and when I got out there, the house looked empty. What's going on?"

"Well, since you haven't been here, I had to sell the house."

"Is that right? Well, you don't have to sell the house. I know I started the paper work, but I'm going to be fine." While we drove to the restaurant, I sat there getting upset, tripping. *"It's been since May, and you want to call me now after I called you everyday? You think I'm some puppy?"* is what was going on in my mind. I kept the conversation calm, since we were driving on the freeway, "What's wrong? What's up? What is his name?"

Chapter 30

"It ain't no him."

"It's somebody. Look at our kids in the back seat. Look at what you're destroying. I'm not asking you for much. I'm just asking you to be a wife. Is that too much? My basic concerns are, since you don't work, you could cook the kids' dinner, be home when I get home. I leave at 4am in the morning and don't get home till 8pm or 9pm. Just give me Saturday or Sunday so we can have family time. When I call, answer the phone. Just the basic rights that we're supposed to have in a marriage."

"You just try to control too much."

"I don't try to control nothing but, we are married and I have a responsibility and a duty as your husband, and you have a responsibility and a duty as a wife. We have a responsibility and duty as parents."

"That's the problem you always trying to tell me what I'm suppose to do. I do what I want to do."

"You called me, so let's just have a good time. I'm not about to argue with you."

I could feel myself getting angry wondering why I agreed to meet them. I looked in the back seat at my kids, and felt the love I had for them and this woman, no matter how mad she made me. I knew my responsibility as a man, as a husband.

We made it to Dave and Busters and had a great time. It gave me hope.

Don't Play With Me

Over the next couple of months everything was going smooth. We had a nice Halloween and carried on into November. I don't know why but it seemed like every time we started getting along, she wanted to act a fool. Satan was at work again. I kept praying that my marriage would work. I don't remember how this argument started, but it was way foul, way foul. It got to the point were she said, "You get on my mothafuckin' nerves. If being a Christian is anything like you, I don't ever want to be a Christian."

Whoa. "Father, Lord. I need to get out of this because I don't want to be the cause of her loosing her soul."

The next week we were back and forth at each other. One night I was lying in bed with her and Satan jumped up in me, and I told her, "You know what? Let me just get up and wash you the fuck off of me." That's how my skin was crawling. "I'm out." I bounced. I wasn't about to deal with that again, so I went back to my little place.

The next few months rolled by and she called me telling me she sold the house. She told me where they moved to, and I was talking to her still trying to make it work. We were heading into December. I lived in an apartment, but was hardly ever there since I didn't like the area. Entering 2004 would be my second year free.

Deborah called me, and there I was again, back out there trying to make it work. Christmas we were in the new spot, I fried a turkey, mad ham, yams, Mac and cheese. The kids

Chapter 30

had a nice Christmas. Things seemed to be working in the new house. The old house had a lot of evil demons, evil spirits so maybe that's why it didn't work. I blessed the new house and we went through the motion. Everything was working out. I was feeling good again.

2004 started off with the wife, the kids. The paralegal was calling me asking me what to do about the paper work. I told her everything had worked its self, but don't just stop the procedure with the divorce, because we still weren't sure. We were basically playing little kid games over the last little seven, eight months together, not together.

I wasn't really feeling it. When we had sex we were just in the motion of having sex. Sex, to me, was a big issue. When I had to get up, I had to go to work. I came home, paid all the bills. She got to do whatever she wanted while I was gone. All I asked was to give me some loving. I'll break it down to you like this: When you read the bible some things are taken the wrong way. Sometimes the bible is what it is. Back in the old times, the wedding ring signifies something. When a couple makes love, you consummate the marriage with the blood of the virgin. That blood solidified the marriage according to some laws or religions.

In 1 Corinthians 7, Verse 1-5, Advice to the Married, it says, "Now in regard to the matters about which you wrote: 'it is a good thing for a man not to touch a woman,' but because of the cases of immorality, every man should have his own wife, and every woman her own husband. The husband should fulfill his duty toward his wife, and likewise the wife toward her husband. A wife does not have authority over her own body, but rather her husband, and similarly a husband does not have authority over his own body, but rather his wife. Do not deprive each other except perhaps by mutual consent for a time, to be free for prayer, but then return to one another, so that Satan may not tempt you through your lack of self-control."

When I first read this, I realized that sex was really important in the matter of marriage. It's not the most important thing but most men are very sexual creatures. I'm sure most of you readers are saying, "Man, brother. Amen to that." Women readers might think, "Yeah, sounds like my husband, boyfriend, most of the men I've been with." Men are pretty simple, so most issues in a marriage for a man will be based on sex. Sex, to me, in my relationship, in my marriage, is important as long as the respect is there, and the honor is there. The deal breaker in marriage is sex. I have to be happy, sexually.

Deborah and I met November 4th 1988. Every month since we had been together, even when I was in prison, she got a card on the 4th of every month, and flowers throughout the month. After 16 years of getting a card every month and flowers, coming home after a hard days work, I cook, I clean, I didn't ask for much, I was out and busting my butt, I work

Chapter 30

hard, providing and taking care of my family. All I asked was to give me what I can't give myself. Rub my back sometimes, run my bath water. I'm not a nympho. Two or three days a week of great sex and I'm cool. Keep a man happy sexually and you pretty much don't have anything to worry about. Women on the other hand need to be pleased mentally, physically, spiritually, financially. I was covering pretty much every basic need on every level that there was to be covered. No one should have to argue or fight over a basic need.

I walk out again, and this time I got a little one bedroom apartment. My hope was gone. I was done and moving on. I begged for almost a year, been walked over pretty much a year so I was done this time. The phone calls slowed and I was on my own.

Chapter 31

Broke Down In Tears

I met a cool female whose name I don't remember. We met one night, after the club. We talked and hung out for a while and things went really cool. We went to Sea World, out to dinner. This is what I did to put my wife to the side, and get her out of my mind. It was working. I got my own place, started going to the skating ring every week and 2004 was brightening up, going real smooth. My paralegal was telling me the divorce procedure was going smooth. *"Thank you Lord."*

I started getting attached to my new buddy. I slipped back into this mind of wanting to be married. It was ironic because with every woman I met, I found myself talking about marriage, relationships, acting like a desperate person, like I didn't know what was going on out there. This scared

Chapter 31

her off. She let me know, "We moving too fast, we kind of need to slow down." I agreed, but in contradiction, she gave me a key to her place, letting me know I was welcome to come over anytime. She had a nice little career, so, I thought she must be used to dealing with suckas.

It took me a minute, but I started putting it all together. I didn't need a key to her place. We were hangin' out, havin' a ball, she was by my place I went by her place, she was cool, she had a cool job, nice spot, nice car. The street in me started kickin' in and it all added up to, "Baby girl got a dude, or somebody she's messing with," since, there were times when she just disappeared for a minute. I got at her, and asked, "What's up? You seeing somebody?" She said, "Well, not really." Okay, any time you start off, "Not really," that means, "Hell, yes!" I was cool and told her, "What we gone do is, we really are going to slow down." I knew she was feelin' me, and I was feelin' her, but she already had what she needed, but what she *wanted,* was me. I'm a sweet, sensitive guy, you know, caring guy and a loving guy. That's what she wanted. But she needed somebody to pay her bills, her car note, her fly lifestyle. She had both worlds. At that point, I let her have the world she *needed.*

That night I was just out there, feeling bad. I felt real low. I got to my apartment complex, walked around the pool and Jacuzzi, sat by the pool and looked in the water at the shimmering lights. When I really want to think I usually get in my car and drive, put on some nice slow music and just zone out. I walked from the pool, back to my car, drove off, and zoned out, breaking down in tears. "Father, Lord. Please. I need help. I'm lost out here. I'm stuck Lord. Let me live. You said be in the world and not of the world. Father, I'm not even in the world right now. I'm so confused and lost God. My divorce, I didn't want it but it is here. I tried to make this relationship work with this girl. It didn't work. I don't want to be out here just having sex, and wilding out. I can see that life coming and I'm fighting these demons off me. I need your help Father, Lord. Just let me live. Let me live, please Lord." At that point, the tears just stopped flowing and I felt pretty good.

The next day I woke up, and things were cool. I was feeling like a new man. One of my buddies came by. She said, "Kevin, you kind of changed a little bit. You ain't that person that I saw last year. When we were talking to each other you talked about marriage and relationships, and I just had to bounce. You were a little too deep for me."

Believe it or not, that's how my life had been going. things were going smooth and everything was working itself out and it was all…. Good.

May 2004, I was at the skating ring. As I was skating, I bumped into this little chick, and said I was sorry. She looked at me all crazy. "I didn't try to do it. What's your name?"

Chapter 31

She told me her name and I told her mind. She said, "You use to date my sister along time ago."

"what?"

"Yeah, you use to date my sister."

"Who's your sister?"

She told 'em her sister's name. "Aww, man! That's my little light bright. I've been looking for her for a while ever since I've been out here dating. Call her."

We got off the floor and she called but her sister didn't answer. So I asked for her number and gave her mine to give her sister. A few months prior, I ran into Light Bright's dude at the skating rink, who told me they weren't together anymore but they were still cool. I asked him to give her my number but he never did. It's crazy how life works. When I first met light bright, her sister couldn't have been much older than 11. She used to peek around the corner, and giggle when she saw me. It's funny that she would remember me all these years. That's how God works. She mentioned that her sister was working at UCLA Harbor Medical Center. When I got home I tried calling her and left her a message. I thought about her all night.

The next morning while I was at work, I got a phone call from her. I asked what was going on. We had a little conversation but she was just getting off of work and was tired. She had a dance class that evening and would be free by 7pm. So I planned to call her after work. I still had my

Broke Down In Tears

Saturn that my homeboy bought me, and the Lexus. I told my sister, "Man, I haven't seen Monica in probably 7 years. Should I go over there looking like a bum, in my work close or what?" She hadn't seen me in a while, and I just want to play it like that, looking like regular old blow Joe. My sister advised me not to go over there like that because I never know how she is. "You're right. I just don't really feel like putting on no clothes."

"Kevin, I'm just saying. She's probably not going to be tripping off of that, but she hasn't seen you in a while, so just put on some clothes."

"You're right."

I went and got a fresh hair cut, put on the gear. Brother was looking nice, smooth bald head. I'm a brown skin cat, nice brown eyes about 5'6, nice little build, about 140, work out 3 or 4 days a week. I threw on a white guess shirt, with some Kenneth Cole shoes, black Guess Jeans, nice little boot cut at the bottom. A brother was looking real smooth. I got the fresh manicure with the nails buffed, popped on my Mavoto. When I pulled up I saw her, *"Damn, little light bright done picked up a little weight since I seen her last."*

Last time I saw her, she was going through problems with her dude so she was really thin. She lost a lot of weight, but was still cute. She just looked at me, gazing in my eyes. All the memories were coming back, when we went paint balling, visited the haunted house, of all the fun we had. She

303

Chapter 31

wasn't just a girl I was having sex with that I didn't care about. It was at the time in my life I had kids and Deborah. I couldn't get serious with her cause since she was young and I didn't want to hurt her. I pretty much just played around and never wanted to cross that line with a relationship with her. Who knows what life will bring? I didn't want to hurt her. I was always honest with her back then.

Now I was single, and she was single. We had dinner. I told her about the kids, about my family, my situation, my wife, that I was married but going through a divorce, that I was looking to be married again, about wanting more kids. I opened the door to my whole life. I explained my expectations in a marriage, and the sex issue I've just discussed. I didn't go into too much detail about sex with her since I remembered what we had, and the sex was the bomb. I asked her what she wanted. She told me she was looking for a relationship with somebody that's cool, and caring.

Over the next few weeks things were going smooth. The loving was great any time I wanted sex. She came over my house, I'd cook dinner for her. We rubbed on each other, watched T.V together, movies together. We were real intimate. She'd rub my back, real affectionate, real sweet. When I called, she answered my phone calls. She'd call to say, "Hey, Kevin I'm going here, I'm going there. I'll be home at this time." She was giving me everything I wanted. In a month's time, I proposed to her. We hooked back up in

Broke Down In Tears

May, and I proposed to her in June. I was rushing things. The night I proposed to her, she said yes. I asked her to move in with me. My son wanted to live with me so I moved into a 2 bedroom apartment. He'd be moving in, in July. We had the perfect little family. Everything was going fine. I was loving it. I hadn't thought about my soon to be ex-wife.

I was happy I had my son, but the part hurt was that my wife was still tripping. I had my kids every weekend since I left the first time in 2003. Now that I had Monica, my fiancée, in my life, my wife got salty, and decided to keep the kids from me. I couldn't talk to them on the phone, I couldn't visit. I left messages saying, "I thought we said that if we ever separated, we wouldn't use the kids against one another. Look at what you're doing." I couldn't believe it.

In the meantime, my fiancé was being supportive. Everything was going fine until she did a flip on me, a complete flip. "Your sister calls you all the time. Your homeboys call you too much. You need to stop having them call." I couldn't believe she was really saying this to me. No big deal. I wanted to see just how selfish she was because I had never seen this side of her. I was going to play alone in the game. I asked my sister to stop calling me, "My fiancé don't like it that much so, you know, stop calling me." I told my homeboys I'd holler at them later. I turned my phone off. I was home by 6:00pm. I was being a good boy. She was eating this up. In her mind, she was thinking, "I got this

305

Chapter 31

nigga sprung." 10 years ago, the only time we spent together was going out, having sex, and some phone conversation. It wasn't enough to really know a person. We started making plans. We put the deposit down on the wedding, and everything was going as fine as it could. By late July things were really heating up. I hadn't seen my kids since I met her. My wife still wouldn't let me see them. This is the crazy twist   that   came   into   my   life.

Chapter 32

Her Last Breath

My mother went into the hospital, sometime in mid-July. She had gone into the hospital 6 months prior, when I noticed she looked sick. I didn't say anything to anybody. This time I knew once she went in, she wasn't coming out. I knew this in my heart and mind.

One day Monica and I went to a location we planned to be married in. I'm an older cat so I was sharp, with my slacks, nice little shoes, nice little belt to match the shoes, nice little shirt. She asked me, "Why do you have that on? Take it off." "Yeah..right!" I thought. "No!" I said. So she tripped, with an attitude the whole way to Westwood. The entire time we shopped she didn't want me to touch her, nothing. It was all funny to me. I had been popping her on the butt. I like to pop my woman on the butt here and there. "STOP," she was yelling, "I don't like that. Stop! Just stop! Damn!" She was just cranky. She started acting like my ex-wife. I was really bugging out.

One day I accidentally called her my daughter's name. She got mad about that. It was my daughter's name, not my wife's. These were the battles we went through. My mom was in the hospital, I proposed to Monica, I couldn't see my kids. August came around and my daughter and son went to visit my mom in the hospital. Deborah let them come home with me. I planned to take them to the movies. I hadn't seen my daughter, so I was hugging her, talking to her. My fiancé was getting jealous, and mad. I could see it in her face. I was trying to make both of them happy, by dividing my attention. But it wasn't working. It was an uncomfortable day, at the movies.

When I got home I lay on the bed, barred my face and started crying. I thought she was the one, but was realizing she wasn't. I was hurt and torn. "What's wrong?" she asked. I told her what was wrong and she said, "It ain't that. I just haven't seen you with any other person."

"This is my daughter. You tripping."

Her Last Breath

The next day I was up at the hospital. Everything was going cool. I was really hoping Monica wasn't pregnant but I had a feeling she was.

Things got real bad one night at dinner. My son said, "Dad did they use to call you Nino."

"Yeah, but that's something totally different."

Monica said, "Yeah, they use to call him Nino. Where is Nino at? Bring Nino back."

"Look you couldn't handle Nino if you wanted to back then, and you definitely couldn't handle Nino now."

I was letting her push my buttons, acting like a little wimp, a little punk. The breaking point was when I continued to visit my mom, and she started sweating me, "Why do you have to go to see your mom?"

"That's it. I'm done. We're not getting married. The marriage is off. I'm done. I want you out of my place."

"I'm not going nowhere."

The next day she rode with me to the hospital. She wouldn't leave. I had my son and my nephew in the car, and we had a big argument. When I got back, I yelled, "GET THE FUCK OUT OF MY SHIT RIGHT THE FUCK NOW! I'm tired of your mothafuckin' shit! You sit up here and run your mothafuckin' mouth too fucking much. Get the fuck out!"

"I don't have to go nowhere."

Chapter 32

So she had to work one Saturday, and when she left, I changed the locks. She couldn't get back in. she called, "Kevin, I can't get in the place."

"I know. I changed the locks." This was around October.

"I'm tired of your shit. I let you take my relationship away from my sister and me. I let you run my friends away. I let you try to ruin my relationship with my daughter. Now my mom is in the hospital and you're tripping off me going to the hospital. This is my momma. I touch you, you curse me out. You don't want to cook like you said you would. You ain't been cleaning up shit. You didn't want to do none of the stuff you suckered my ass into. You ain't been doing none of them.

Now, you don't want to have sex. I didn't ask for this shit. If I wanted this shit I would have stayed married with my mothafuckin' wife. You came along with false advertising like a mothafuckin' car lot. I go to pick out a car it say power windows, power locks, cruise control, A/C, power brakes, leather. I'm paying for a fully equipped car then find out it doesn't have power locks, power windows, cruise control, A/C. It ain't got shit. That's what the fuck you turned out to be. I'm tired of your mothafuckin' shit."

With all of the pressure, I finally snapped. I couldn't do anything about my wife not letting me see my kids. I couldn't go to court for it. The divorce was already costing more than I had. I couldn't do anything about my momma in the hospital. I couldn't do anything, besides get rid of her mothafuckin' ass. She was done. She was out. "Let me know when you want to come get your shit and that's it." Click.

Another blow to me was that I found out she was pregnant. I just left my family, and now I had another on the way. The shit was bugging me out.

The next week went by and I was doing me. I was dating my little Hispanic. We were having a ball, having great sex. I was meeting girls at the skating rink. I was doing me now. I went back to the streets man but I wasn't out there selling dope. I felt like, "Fuck the whole mothafuckin' world!" The world hurt me, my wife hurt me, my momma was in the hospital still, so I had a 'Fuck you' attitude. I cut emotions off. I wasn't getting hurt by anybody else. I was back out there wilding out.

Monica called me one day, "Where you going?"

"To the hospital."

"Can I come up there?"

"Sure."

So she came up there. I told my mom she was pregnant. She touched her stomach and said, "It's a boy!" My momma lit up, all happy. My mom couldn't really speak by this time. They told us she had a mass in her throat but they didn't know what it was. They had to wait for the biopsy to come back.

Chapter 32

I continued to have fun with several women, including the Hispanic broad through November. I was at the hospital every night, watching my mom slowly leaving us. While we were at the hospital, my pops and sister were up there, the whole family. My moms was never left alone. They finally told my moms that she was dying. My mother used to drink a lot. Se said, "Well, if I'm dying, let me go home and get me a drink." My father didn't want to let moms go home. Everyone told her to stay in the hospital. I told everyone, "Just let her come home." Everyone held hope that she would be healed. The doctor already done said she was dying. I had already thought she wouldn't be coming home. She had esophageal cancer. I cried. They performed a tracheotomy on my mom. A tracheotomy is done to open an air passage for breathing in the throat. When I first saw it, I started yelling at the doctors, "What is this!" I started going off. The doctors explained what it was, telling me I had to calm down.

Because of her drinking, one day in the hospital she started shaking and rocking in withdrawal. When I was in prison, I took a mandatory drug class that described alcoholics. Alcoholism is one of the worst addictions to man, next to heroin. They are the two hardest addictions to kick. Going off cold turkey causes black outs and withdrawal. It reminded me of why my father couldn't remember beating my mother. I watched my mom have these break downs because she went cold turkey. I told the doctor to give her something, but they said it wasn't prescribed. Eventually they gave her something that calmed her down.

She was at UCLA Harbor, which is where the interns do their residency. They practiced cutting on her and my dad let them. I wanted them to stop. My mother got to be so bad, she went on life support. Her birthday was October 23. My brother and pops arranged to bring candles and a cake to the hospital. They misunderstood who was getting what, so they ended up getting into a bad argument, almost ready to throw blows at each other. We all had to step between them. We were at the hospital acting like this, fighting and arguing constantly, back and forth. It wasn't cool. Thanksgiving was here and the family was breaking apart. I was going off on my sister, talking bad to the whole family. We were going off on the nurses and doctors. Imagine loosing your mother.

One night back at my apartment, I was laying there by my self praying, "Father, Lord. When is it going to stop? My life is rough. I went from prison, loosing my family, loosing my new fiancé, and now I'm loosing my momma." I had been under pressure since 1996. I was running out of feelings and emotions. My fiancé was telling me about the baby. I told her, "Look, I don't want this baby." She didn't want to get an abortion. I was being mean to her. We had nothing to talk about. "Ok, then, just have the baby, and when you have it, I'll holler." My only concern was my momma. That's all that I could think about. I was messed up over those few

313

months. December rolled around. They wanted to operate on my mother some more. Everything was just falling apart on her. Her bladder was backing up, and they want to go in there and try to do something with that. My dad kept okaying them. I said, "Dad, come on now. Stop." My dad stuck with my mom for 42 years. He hadn't been the best husband. I thought, "You didn't let her live in peace. At least let her die in piece." I told my sister I didn't condone the treatment. "Quit letting them treat my momma like a chopping block. Quit letting her be a guinea pig, stick this tube in her, stick that tube in her, slice her up, biopsy this. Quit letting them experiment on my momma. Quit letting them operate." I didn't have any say, but I could look at my mom and see she wasn't there anymore. That was not my mother, only her body. "Dad, however you loved her, you loved her. It's too late. You can't make up for it right now. Whatever you didn't do as a husband, you can't now." My sisters didn't have a good relationship with my mom. I told them, "Whatever daughter you were or weren't, whatever y'all had, whatever disagreements y'all had, you can't make up for this now. This is my momma right here." I loved my momma. I was the best son that I could be. I had no regrets. I had no guilt. Whatever my momma wanted, I gave my momma. I saw my momma in pain and I told her she was going to be alright.

Her Last Breath

I had a brother in jail fighting his case, and he was trying to get home, to spend whatever time he could with my mom, talking to her over the phone.

The final operation didn't work so now my mom was out and with no movement. They made her a vegetable. I watched my father in pain as he lost his wife. I could only imagine it from the pain of my divorce on September 22nd, in 2004 right on my birthday. I was feeling my dad's pain. I knew, despite his abuse, and other women, that this man loved this woman.

"Father, Lord. I'm sorry. You know I've been hard on my dad. You know I'm looking at my sister's and I'm looking at their pain. It's hard on them. Lord, please let me loosen up because I feel their pain."

I didn't have these kinds of emotions. In my life, I dealt with reality. I knew that my mom was not coming out of this. I just wanted them to let her go so she wouldn't suffer any more.

We were all there on Christmas. We were there every night supporting each other, through the arguments, through the pain, through everything. We were a family. We might tell each other how we feel, we might cut each other up with words, but I guarantee we love each other. And loving each other- That's what family is about.

Chapter 32

When my mom passed, it hit everybody. I just start crying, shedding tears. But I saw the glory and the beauty when my mom passed. I watched her take her last breathe.

We can't be hard on ourselves when our parents pass. We are supposed to bury our parents.

I watched her first heart beat as she was born again unto Christ. She left this body and she was reborn. I watched this transformation. It was beautiful for me. I was at peace. It wasn't a phone call in the middle of the night that your mother just got hit by a car, or a bullet went into her head, or a heart attack. There was no wondering. We had months to prepare for this. God gave us a glorious gift. We were together as a family, my dad, sisters, brother, my mother's sister, brother-in-law, nieces, nephews, me and the entire family, when they took my mother off life support. This is what I told my dad.

I was going through all of this, and I called my ex-fiancé, to inform her of my mother's passing. I call my ex-wife and I told her she passed and that I just needed somebody to be with. Deborah came over and we ended up hanging out, chilling with my daughter. We kicked back and had a cool time. This is what family should have been about. We talked for the next day or two and then it was back to her shaking me and running the streets.

2005, I wanted to try to make it work with my family. My son would be here soon, but I didn't know him. We

Her Last Breath

wouldn't be together. I was trying to think about my other kids, but my ex-wife and I weren't together. My whole life was crazy. Nothing else could hurt me in this world. God could do anything, but as far as this world, it couldn't do anything else to me that hadn't already been done.

Chapter 33

We Can See My Son's Hair

2005 came and I saw how Deborah was living with my kids. She got rid of her car, and was out there driving something raggedy, with water flooding the floor. She was living crazy, with her mother. I told her, "You can't keep living like this. Come on and stay with me." From there we were working things out. We spent Valentines Day together. It wasn't a real relationship, but I was still feeling her. I didn't know if she was feeling me, but I hoped there was a chance.

I wasn't feeling my ex-fiancé. I told her everything about my past, up front. I told her what I had been through with my ex-wife what I expected. She said she wouldn't do it then turned around and acted worse than my ex-wife. Looking back now, she was probably going through hormonal changes, since she was pregnant and I wasn't aware. But, I didn't car. I didn't have those types of emotions.

Deborah came with me but then decided she wanted to move to Georgia. I told her I'd help her go, but I wouldn't help her come back. By that time, I was looking forward to getting my ex-wife to Georgia so I could just go back to doing me, and having a ball. I wasn't feeling any relationship, my mom was gone, and I wanted peace in my life. For the first time, I needed peace.

When Deborah left, my son went with her. I couldn't let him stay the way he was doing in school. I was doing the best I could, meeting with his teachers. I warned him that if he got C's he wouldn't get anything for Christmas. He got C's and didn't get anything. He called his mother, "This isn't fair. Dad won't get me nothing for Christmas." So she came to get him. I warned her not to come get him because I knew what he needed. I told my son, "I had you with me because you didn't want to live with your mom. I told you, you can't go back and forth." By that time he was crying, "Dad I want to stay with you."

They stuck with the plans to move to Georgia, and my son went with them.

I was just enjoying my life. I got a phone call one day. I didn't answer. Monica's mom left a message going off on me. I called Monica and told her to talk to her mom because I didn't know what she was calling about. Monica said after

Chapter 33

she got her things from my house, she was missing one shoe and her Louie Vouttain purse, her degree, diploma, someone poured bleach all over her clothes, and ripped up her clothes, "Okay, I'm sorry. I didn't know this but if you would have came and got your shit when I told you. The only reason I'm talking to you like this is, because your mom just called me talking crazy. I respect you but things would have been different if she didn't come at me like that. Talk to your mom and tell her not to call me like that." She apologize and we worked it out... click... I hung up.

My mother's funeral was in January. I get through February. My son was due in May. I still wasn't feeling my ex-fiancé. I was doing me, and time was rolling around. I shot out to Georgia to make sure my kids were living okay. Spent time with Deborah. I helped them set up. I went back out there about 3 weeks later and she told me we couldn't keep doing this. I wasn't tripping. I was basically trying to make sure there was no hope of getting back together. I thought with the distance, things could work out differently. But it wasn't working, so I was cool.

I was getting ready to come out there another time and she tell me not to come. I was really trying to make sure they were okay because they just moved to a place were they didn't know anyone. But she was coming at me shady and side ways. So that was it. I was cool.

We Can See My Son's Hair

I was laying up one night thinking about my ex-fiancé. I loosened up so she was coming back around. She apologized to me, after seeing her mistake. She saw what she did wrong. I was being hard on her and thinking that I needed to really give her another chance. We hooked back up and started going out again, to the movies, dinner. She was happy. She really wasn't that bad. She just made a mistake. In the story of Joeb, everything was taken from him. He was tested and stayed faithful to God. That's how I was looking at my life. I broke off the engagement but I still really loved her. I wasn't really doing her wrong.

When I cut my emotions off it was like a light switch. They came on and they went off. Once I turned them off, that was it. I learned how to move on. After doing almost five years in prison, then going through all I went through, my emotions had to be in control. If not this stuff was enough to make me go crazy.

I was lying up thinking I could possibly have a good future with her as long as we could get on the same page. I was hoping she would understand me and how I felt. I gave her the benefit of the doubt, not with the intention of being together, but at least to loosen up.

My son was due May 22nd, which was my younger brother's birthday. I had to prepare myself mentally for a new child. My youngest son was about to turn 8. I moved back into a 1 bedroom apartment. I was having fun dating,

321

doing me, hanging out, just doing whatever I wanted to do. I slipped back a little bit trying to mess with the music industry again. It wasn't going to well. All my cats were doing well, Brian, Steve and another cat named Big Jon. These were the only contacts I had. Big Jon was head of Music Publishing at EMI. I told them I wasn't really looking. I just want to get back in the music industry. I told Big Jon that I was doing catering, and he turned me on to some big catering jobs over at EMI. He opened the door and he was cool because he remembered me, you know when we were hanging out trying to make things work with Craig. One day I got at Big Jon, "Check this out. I'm not asking you for nothing. I've been away from the music industry for a while and it's different now. I'm thinking about getting back into it. I got this cat I think is good. I want you to listen to him and tell me know if he's worth my time."

Big John had that country accent, "Yeah, I can do that." So I went to get the CD called Big John told him I was sending it to him. I waited until I knew he got the CD, and I called him. The secretary said Big Jon wasn't there, and if I could leave him a message. "Just tell him Kevin is on the phone." She put me on hold. She had just told me he wasn't there. So she came back and I left a message. Couple days went by and I didn't hear from him, so I hit him on his cell and left another message, "Big Jon, I thought we was better than that, dawg. I'm still me I'm still the same dude from

We Can See My Son's Hair

back in the day when we both was coming up. I'm not asking you for nothing. I'm not like all these other dudes, jocking you. I basically just needed your opinion from your ear, because you out here. You done signed Jay-Z, Usher had your hands on Alicia Keys. I know you got the ear for this deal. I don't know if my ear is there or not. You ain't got to play me like this, like I'm some girl jocking you or some of these dudes in the streets. I'm the same cat that you use to come up to EMI when you were trying to get hired, running behind my tail, so I mean come on, dawg."

I got a call back, "Aww man it ain't like that."

"I'm just saying, you know, don't treat me like that. I thought we had a better relationship than that."

"Alright, man. When I get back in town I'm going to listen to it and give you a call."

"Okay, cool."

He said he'd be back in a week. I let time go by, and in the meantime, I was working on Monica and me. We were still talking over the phone, about the baby, what we were going to name him, how things were going to be, how he was going to be. Everyone was happy, waiting to see this new grandbaby. He was a new child coming into the world, someone that could bring the family together. Over the weeks I felt that the music industry could improve my catering business. I could dip into the music while catering. I was feeling good. That was outside the fact that my ex-wife was bugging now, ever since Monica came into my life. I still had a hard time communication with my kids.

That week went by and I didn't hear from Big Jon. I called, he didn't answer. I called his secretary and left a message. I called him again and left him a message, "You know what, dawg. You told me you would holler at me in about a week and that didn't really go down. But I see how it is. I'm not about to chase you, man. I wish you the best endeavor in your future. Hopefully things pan out. Maybe you will treat me with a little better respect like I did you.

As I hung up, I thought about how long I had been gone, and how these cat's lives changed. Steve was married to Fred Siegel's daughter. Big Jon was head of EMI music publishing, but he just managing producers when I went to prison. Brian was over at famous publishing, he helped sign Eminem. They had new friends, different types of friends. I was basically nothing to them at that point. It's like 50 cent says "These industry niggas ain't friends. They just know how to pretend." So I understood Big Jon. I wasn't even mad at him. Since he signed Jay-Z and Usher he didn't have to worry about little people like me. He had new nigga nuts to swing from.

It's funny how industry cats are. They find one set of nuts to the next set of nuts. Whoever can help them out. I wasn't that type of dude. I really had love for these dudes and unfortunately it's not like that for them. No disrespect to

324

them. The music industry was basically a legal dope game. Life changed and I was still trying to make it out there and God had blessed me to do well.

I didn't think that I would be affected by that. I really had love for these dudes, man. They were my cats back in the day. I would have died for these dudes. I decided to shake it and forget about the music industry. I focused harder on my catering, and let my life prosper.

Closer to my son's due date, Monica started spending a few nights with me. We had been getting along pretty well. She was being real sweet and nice. I don't know if it was hurting her to do this, bothering her, or if it was an act, or a front. But she was being really sweet. Some things were working themselves out. We weren't in a committed relationship and I wasn't thinking about one. She wanted one but I wasn't there yet. I wasn't feeling her like that. I still didn't have emotions. They were cut off. I closed that door. I didn't even want emotions right now. I just wanted to live.

May 2005. Monica was having her little pains, her stomach was growing, and we were taking pictures, and laughing. It was funny but for me. Pregnant is not cute at all. That's just how I feel. It's pretty, it's beautiful but it's nothing sexy about pregnancy. But for a pregnant woman, she was a beautiful pregnant woman. No stretch marks, healthy. She was blessed. May 22nd approached, and she was

325

Chapter 33

having a few little labor pains but nothing real heavy or strong. She asked me if she could spend the night with me so she wouldn't be somewhere hard for me to get to her. Her mother lived in Stevenson Ranch, about an hour away. The hospital was Long Beach Memorial. I agreed.

The whole weekend of the 21st and 22nd she was having labor pains and contractions. Still, nothing strong. On the 23rd, that Monday, she started having strong contractions. She went to the doctor since she had an appointment and nothing happened. They told her she wasn't dilating yet and her contractions were too far apart, so she wouldn't be admitted. *"Lord here we go again."*

I already had three kids so I had been through this. On the 24th her contractions were 5 minutes apart but she hadn't dilated, but this time they kept her. They told her to walk around the hospital and she started doing that. She had been walking and doing what she was supposed to do. The morning of the 24th went by, and still nothing happened. No dilation. Nothing changed but I stayed. I took the day off work to stay at the hospital. I had a catering event on the 27th, a Memorial Day Party so I was hoping my son would be born that 24th. Her parents and family came up there. Nothing was happening but she was in major pain. I had been through this three times already with my other kids. I had seen my sister have her kids and this was usual for her to be in this kind of pain. Doctors were in an out. She still wasn't dilating. The

We Can See My Son's Hair

24th passed and nothing. On the 25th and she was having contractions anywhere from two to three minutes apart. She should have been dilated by now. I had heard of women having 2 to 3 days labor but this didn't seem right. I felt for her. She was in there crying. The doctors come in there feeling her cervix and she was getting irritated. I was feeling her pain. I felt for her, so I continued to stay. I wanted to see my son. I prayed for her and my son's health. I was nervous. This wasn't cool for her to be in this kind of pain. Why didn't they just take the baby? I ask the doctor how long before they would do a C-section. Monica was a surgical tech so she knew what went on in hospitals. At Long Beach Memorial they have residents.

The morning of the 25th, the nurse came in, and Monica had a major attitude with the nurse. So the nurse didn't come back in there, period. She waited for the doctor later on that day.

"See, you and your mouth."

That night, while she slept, I took another look over my life and prayed, "Lord, Father. I've been through a lot, Lord, and you've blessed me to make it through a lot." I looked back on my childhood. I was a great basketball and football player. I was in the boy scouts. I came from a good home. Despite my parent's fights and drinking, they loved us. Coming up, if somebody would have said, "Kevin you're gonna be one of the biggest drug dealers in Compton," I

327

would have told them, "You're a liar." As a child I wanted to be a police or fireman. That was my dream. The fact that I was a drug dealer was surreal. Out of high school, if somebody would have told me that, I would have told them they were a liar. When I was out there selling drugs, if somebody would have told me, "You're going to jail," I would have said, "I'm not doing anything. They're not getting ready to catch me."

Laying there I remembered the conversations I had with my ex-wife. She was telling my kids that this new baby wouldn't be their brother or sister. I told her not to tell them that because the same blood that was flowing through their body was the same blood flowing through my new son. She was telling them that they didn't have to love this baby. This was *my* baby.

"This is their brother so don't talk to them like this."

I sat there thinking about these conversations and about my son soon to be in this world. I was looking at my girl over there. She was in pain and I couldn't do anything for her. Deborah could take the kids away from me against my will, but they will never have another daddy. I remember telling her.

"You can give them a step daddy, a play daddy, an uncle, a godfather, or whatever you want., but you will never, in life, be able to give them another daddy. I am a good dad, a good man, a good person and you're not going to ever be able to

replace me or what I do for them. You're not going to ever have another man that will do for them, give his life for them, or love them like I love them. He won't care for them like I care for them. Don't do that. Don't take them out of my life."

I thought about when I came home from prison, praying, *"Father, Lord. Just give me a second chance in life, Father, no matter what I do when I come home. I have to start my life completely over. I have to start from nothing."*

This is what I was praying for.

I talked to God in that dark hospital room thinking about my life. "Lord, you have blessed me. You've given me my life back. No, I don't make twenty, fifty, or one hundred thousand dollars in weeks and months but I am making good money." It wasn't about money. I realized this that Christmas in jail and my son wanted me. *"I just want you to come home."*

God was getting ready to give me a new son. I was praying that maybe my ex-wife would wake up and get out of her foolish state and stop telling those children that this new child wasn't going to be a part of them.

Women readers- check yourselves. The hatred for a man shouldn't run so deep to affect your child. How dare you. When men and women separate, a child still needs his/her father. A woman who takes a child away from the father should really change and check your soul, check your spirit, check your mind-set and see. Listen to my words and how I

329

feel as a man. It hurts, I'm telling you. It hurts to have your kids taken away from you because of money.

It's sad that children are taken due to child support. What gives you the right? Because a man can't give you a dollar amount means that he can't do anything for his kids? That isn't right. Look at the generations out here. Look at what is going on. Women have taken on the role of men and we have no leaders. In the old days, men and women raised these kids together. What happened? What went wrong?

I looked at Monica and thought, "No matter what happens between you and me, I just pray to God that she lets me be a part of my boy's life. I hope she doesn't take my child away from me like my ex-wife did. Father Lord, in the name of Jesus, I just want to thank you Father, Lord for giving me my life back, bringing me through prison, all the times that you have saved my life, keeping me from AIDS, and other diseases, from when I went off the side of the freeway. Father, Lord, thank you! Father, Lord, from the day I was born into this world, you've had me in your hands. I want to thank you Father, Lord, for when my abscess burst and the poison went in through my system, I survived. I don't know where my life is headed. I don't know what direction I'm going. I do know that You keep me in Your grace, Your mercy, and that You've always loved me. You kept your arms around me. Father, Lord, when my son comes into this world, I pray that you protect his mother and let him come

We Can See My Son's Hair

into this world a healthy baby. I don't care what he looks like. Father Lord, just bring me a healthy child. A child with no dysfunctions, a child that has all of his fingers and all of his toes, a child that can breathe normally, walk and talk normally, just a healthy child, Father."

I hope the readers of this book will be touched. I hope you can look over your life and ask God to forgive you.

My girl was still in labor. This was a painful labor. Nothing was happening and I had been up all night thinking about my entire life. It was about to start over in this room, with my new son, in my one bedroom apartment.

The sun was rising and I looked over at her and she looked back at me. She woke up in pain. I could see it all over her face.

I dozed off and when I woke up, her mom and aunties were coming back in the room while the nurses are telling her to push. *We would see my son's hair.* She was pushing with all of her strength and nothing was happening and I was feeling so much pain. She was squeezing my arm. I had been through this before, but each time is a new experience. I was helpless. I didn't know what to do. She was pushing, and pushing. Nothing was happening. My son was in trauma and the doctor rushed in. They had a device inside of her to monitor my son to see if there was any pressure and to measure his heart rate. It wasn't good and I was starting to panic. It was all going bad, "Father, Lord. Come on. Please

331

Chapter 33

help her!" They told her she had to have a c-section so they took her in the room, prepped her, and got me ready.

We went into the room, just the doctors and me. I was right beside her thinking, "Lord, he's coming. My son will be here." Everything was ready and they started cutting her stomach and I can remember the smell. It had the scent of fresh blood and flesh, alive and flowing. The doctor pushed on her stomach. The baby wasn't coming out. I could see the doctor moving him around and I was wondering what he was doing. My son wouldn't come out. He just wouldn't come into this world. The doctors kept pushing and tugging and finally, my son came out. The doctor popped him and my son started crying. "Father, Lord. Thank you, in the name Jesus." Monica looked at me smiling and tired. "It's a boy."

"Yes, a boy. A baby boy." I was smiling and happy. I went over to watch him. They took the baby and cleaned him. I was cautious because I almost fainted when my first son was born. I was only 20 years old at that time. My new son was born and I was a man.

I had been through changes in my life. I grew up and I developed a relationship with God. I felt good about this. I went over and cut the umbilical cord. "This is my boy." My ex-wife had snatched my kids like pieces of paper from my hand. But God said, "My son, here goes your new son. I bring you a new baby boy." This is what God was telling me.

We Can See My Son's Hair

As I held my baby boy, this is what God was telling me. I walked over to my girl and handed him to her. We hugged him together. This was all ours. This was our baby. We were a happy family and I smiled. As my son was wrapped, I thought for the first time,

"Father Lord, You're a good God, a graceful and merciful God. Father Lord, I thank you in the name of Jesus. Father I want to thank you for blessing me with a new life, a new son, a new woman. I thank you Father Lord, in the name of Jesus. I thank you for all that you have brought me through. Thank you, Father, for this new glorious life. Thank you Lord. I love You, in Jesus' name, I pray. Amen.